101
things
to do
OUTSIDE

WELDONOWEN
PUBLISHING

WELDONOWEN
PUBLISHING

First published in Great Britain in 2015 by Weldon Owen,
an imprint of the Bonnier Publishing Group.
Kings Road Publishing
3.08 The Plaza, 535 King's Road,
Chelsea, London, SW10 0SZ

© 2015 Weldon Owen. All rights reserved.
www.weldonowen.co.uk
www.bonnierpublishing.com

ISBN: 978-1-78342-020-9

First edition
2 4 6 8 10 9 7 5 3 1

Printed in China

101 things to do OUTSIDE

CONTENTS

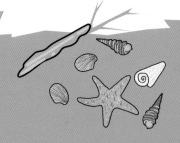

1 ATTRACT BUTTERFLIES

Tempt butterflies into your garden or onto your balcony with a butterfly feeder. It's simple to make and works like a dream.

YOU WILL NEED:

- Paper plate
- Scissors
- String
- Overripe (mushy) fruit

1 Make four holes around the rim of your paper plate. They should be equally spaced, just like the hour, half-past, quarter-past, and quarter-to positions on a clock face.

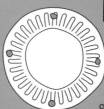

2 Cut four equal lengths of string and double knot the ends. Thread the string through the holes in your plate, making sure that the knots are underneath the plate. Tie the ends of the string together at the top.

3 Chop some overripe fruit and put it onto the plate. Butterflies particularly like squishy banana! (If you put a banana in your refrigerator, it will go black and mushy more quickly.) Now hang up your feeder, and wait for some butterfly visitors!

TOP TIP

Plant flowers to attract butterflies too! Sunflowers are great because butterflies love them!

DONE! DATE COMPLETED

CALCULATE HOW CLOSE A STORM IS

If you like storms, you'll love this! But remember to stay safe. If the storm is overhead, enjoy it from a safe place indoors.

1 On a stormy day, watch out for a flash of lightning in the sky.

2 As soon as you see the lightning, count the number of seconds until you hear the thunder. To be really precise, use a stopwatch. Or be as accurate as you can by counting like this: one-one thousand, two-one thousand, three-one thousand, etc.

3 For every 3 seconds, it is 1 km away (or for every 5 seconds, the storm is 1 mile away). Divide the number of seconds you count to work out the distance.

HOW DOES IT WORK?

Thunder and lightning happen at the same time, but light travels more quickly than sound. The light of the lightning flash travels more quickly than the sound of the thunder.

DONE!　　　DATE COMPLETED

3 GROW PIZZA SAUCE

OK, so you'll need to supply the pizza base and the cheese separately, but you can grow all of the ingredients for a truly delicious pizza sauce in just five to six weeks!

YOU WILL NEED:

- Big container (ideally 30 cm deep) with drainage holes
- Compost
- Plants:
  Tomato, onion, dwarf pepper, basil, chives, thyme, oregano
- Watering can
- Trowel
- Pebbles or sticks
- 3 stakes or bamboo canes
- Garden string

1 Put your container in a sunny spot and fill with compost, leaving 3 cm free at the top. Make sure that your plants are well watered in the containers that they came in.

2 First, plant the tomato. Dig a hole in the centre of the container that is slightly deeper than the tomato plant's pot. Plant the tomato carefully, pressing the soil down around its roots.

3 Divide the pot into six "slices" with your sticks or pebbles. Dig a hole for each plant in a different "slice". Unlike the tomato, the holes should be the same depth as their old pots.

4 If the plant has been in a small pot for a long time, the roots might be packed tightly together. You can carefully pull them apart with your fingertips. But be very gentle!

5 Plant the vegetables and herbs. Make sure that you press the soil down around the roots. The bottom of the stems should be at the same level as the top of the soil. Put labels next to each plant so that you remember which is which.

6 Push the stakes into your container. Space them apart equally, near to the edge. Tie them together at the top like a teepee with garden string. Take care not to disturb your plants. Carefully tie the tomato plant to the sticks, making sure not to tie them too tightly. You just want to tie them so that they can grow upwards and not fall over from the weight of the tomatoes.

7 Keep your pizza garden well watered, and watch it grow. Harvest your crop when it's ready to make an extremely delicious pizza sauce!

DONE! DATE COMPLETED

4 FRAME YOUR DAY

When you next go the beach, take along a camera and snap a few selfies. If your beach allows it, collect shells, pebbles, and other interesting things to take home with you.

YOU WILL NEED:

- Shells and pebbles collected from the beach
- Flat picture frame
- Pencil
- Craft glue

1 When you get home, lay your treasures on the ground outside to see what you've found. You might need to brush off the sand and wash them down before you use them. Pick out the best bits.

2 Arrange your treasures onto the picture frame. Play around with the design until it's exactly how you want it, then glue everything onto the frame with craft glue.

3 Print your best selfie and put it in the frame. What better way to remember a fun day at the beach? It could make a great present, too!

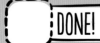
DONE!   DATE COMPLETED

TALK BY TORCH 5

Before satellites, Morse code was used by almost everyone needing to send messages over long distances. It helped to save lives and to win wars. Get together with a friend and give it a try with a torch. It might take longer than texting, but it's a lot of fun!

1 Before dark, you should both practise without the torch. Write messages in dots and dashes on paper, and pass them to each other to decipher. Use the chart below to work out each letter. Keep the messages short and snappy. For example:

INTERNATIONAL MORSE CODE ALPHABET

A •−	J •−−−	S •••	1 •−−−−
B −•••	K −•−	T −	2 ••−−−
C −•−•	L •−••	U ••−	3 •••−−
D −••	M −−	V •••−	4 ••••−
E •	N −•	W •−−	5 •••••
F ••−•	O −−−	X −••−	6 −••••
G −−•	P •−−•	Y −•−−	7 −−•••
H ••••	Q −−•−	Z −−••	8 −−−••
I ••	R •−•		9 −−−−•
			0 −−−−−

2 After dark, send messages with your torches. Stand at either end of a garden or path, and use long flashes for the dashes and short flashes for the dots. If you're receiving the message, write down the dots and dashes on paper so that you can decipher them with the international Morse code alphabet.

6 BOB FOR APPLES

Traditionally a Halloween game, this is great fun on any occasion – you just need a bowl of water and some apples. Be warned, though, you WILL get wet!

1 Put a bowl onto something sturdy at roughly waist height, like a strong outdoor table. Fill it three-quarters full with water and float the apples on the top. Add as many apples as will fit, but not so many that they can't move around in the water.

2 Players must put their hands behind their backs while trying to catch an apple between their teeth. Decide how long each player has – for example, 20 seconds. All other players should count them down by saying one-Mississippi, two-Mississippi, and so on.

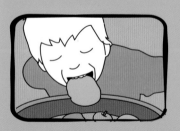

3 When a player has caught an apple, the counting stops and that is their score. Everyone takes a turn, and the person with the lowest score wins!

DONE!   DATE COMPLETED

PLAY SAY AND CATCH

For this game you need a soft ball, some friends, and quick reactions, so make sure to stay alert!

1 Before starting the game, decide on a category – e.g., animals, pop music, beach, school, etc. To begin the game, all stand in a circle at least 1 metre away from one another.

2 Take it in turns to throw the ball to another player. Before catching the ball, each player must say a word that has something to do with the chosen category. So, if the category is animals, they might say "cat". Words can only be used once!

3 Anyone who drops the ball, doesn't come up with a word from the category, or repeats a word that's already been used is out of the game.

4 The last player standing is the winner. Now, choose a different category for a new round!

DONE!   DATE COMPLETED

8 MAKE A SEASHELL PET

Next time you're on the beach, collect shells to take home. Try to find different shapes and sizes, and make sure there aren't any creatures left inside!

YOU WILL NEED:

- A collection of shells
- Craft glue
- Paintbrush
- Modelling clay
- Small beads

1 Take a look at these shell creatures. Are any of them cute enough to be your pet? Use them as inspiration as you sift through your shell collection to find shapes and sizes that you could use.

2 Experiment with different shell combinations before glueing them together. Modelling clay is a great way to fix them in position while you get your glue ready. Build the heads and bodies separately, and glue on smaller parts, like eyes, ears, and noses before joining them to the other bits. If you don't have any tiny shells for eyes and noses, you can use beads.

3 When you're happy with your arrangement, glue it together. Use the brush to paint glue onto the more delicate pieces. The clay is also useful to support your pet while it dries.

DONE!

DATE COMPLETED

PHOTOGRAPH THE ALPHABET

When you're out and about, either in the city or the countryside, find and collect your very own alphabet. If you look carefully, letters are everywhere, even in the most unexpected places.

1 Go for a walk in your neighbourhood to begin the letter hunt. Always take an adult with you, or let one know where you're going. First of all look for the obvious letters on signs, stores, and cars. When you see a letter that you like the look of, take a photo of it. Try to capture just the letter without anything else around it.

2 Now look for less obvious letters. There are lots of shapes in buildings, plants, and all sorts of objects that look like different letters. The letter "E" might be half a window frame or a gate, a set of traffic lights, or the shadow of some telephone lines.

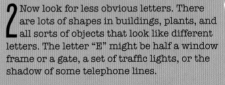
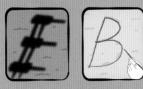

3 Then, make your own letters. You might trace them in the sand or the earth, or you might lay them out with leaves and pine cones or paper clips and pens. You could even ask a friend to make the shape of a letter with his or her body.

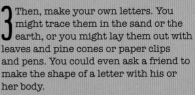

4 Try to collect the whole alphabet. Then, print them out to write messages to your friends. They're great for interesting greetings cards, and especially impressive on valentines!

DONE!

DATE COMPLETED

10 TRY CHINESE JUMP ROPE

For this ancient Chinese game, you'll need skipping elastic and two friends. Stay focused and you might complete all three levels!

1 Decide which two of you are the "enders". If you're the ender, then stand with the elastic around your ankles and feet shoulder-width apart. Be far enough away from each other for the elastic to be pulled tight above the ground.

2 The third person is the jumper. Start with your feet inside the rope, in the middle of the "enders".

3 Jump with both feet out. Then jump with both feet back in.

4 Jump so the right foot lands on the rope, and the left foot lands outside it. Do this again, but the other way around with the left foot on the rope, and the right foot outside it.

5 Jump so that both feet land on the rope. If you've completed this without missing a step or standing on the elastic when you shouldn't have, you've completed level 1!

6 For level 2, the enders lift the elastic to calf height, and the jumper tries to complete the sequence again. If at any point the jumper misses a step or stands on the elastic, it's someone else's turn, and the jumper and ender swap places.

7 Don't worry if you have to swap – it'll be your turn again soon, and you can start from where you left off. See if you can get to level 3, which is knee height. The winner is the first to complete all levels.

WHY NOT?
When you've played levels 1–3, you can try levels 4 and 5, where the rope is at mid-thigh and thigh-high level. Can you jump that high?

DONE!

DATE COMPLETED

11 PLAY GLOW-IN-THE-DARK RING TOSS

Have you ever played glow-in-the-dark ring toss? All you need are a few empty drink bottles, a bunch of glow sticks (30 cm and 15 cm long), and a couple of friends. How good is your aim?

1 Wait until dark. Fill each bottle three-quarters full with water. Bend and shake 6 smaller glow sticks to activate them. Drop 1 into each bottle. Screw on the bottle tops.

2 Each player should now take 5 to 10 of the longer glow sticks and their connectors and make them into rings. Bend and shake them to activate the glow.

3 Set the bottles about 30 cm apart, in a triangular shape. Decide on your throwing line and all stand behind it.

4 Now play! Take it in turns to use all your rings to get as many points as possible. You get 3 points for each ring that lands over a bottle, and 1 point for a ring that touches a bottle. Remember to keep behind the throwing line!

DONE! DATE COMPLETED

SPRAY A RAINBOW

You might not find a pot of gold, but you can make your own rainbow on a sunny day with a garden hose.

1 Check with an adult that it's OK to use the hose before you start. Find a sunny spot to hold the hose, and turn the tap on.

2 Turn until your back is facing the sun. You can check your position by making sure that your shadow is in front of you.

3 Put your thumb over the nozzle to create a misty spray. Hold the hose out in front of you and turn slowly. Keep your thumb over the nozzle, and watch for a rainbow to appear in the spray!

DONE!   DATE COMPLETED

13 BUILD A WILLOW TUNNEL

For a shady retreat, build a willow tunnel. Once
you've got the hang of it, you could also try a
dome. Or build a willow complex, joining domes
and tunnels together!

YOU WILL NEED:

For a 3.5-metre tunnel

- 26 stems of heavy willow for
  the uprights, and another 12 for
  the horizontal walls.
  (available from a garden centre)
- Spade
- Tape measure
- Garden string

1 Decide where you will do this.
Always make sure that you
have permission to use the land.
Now prepare the site. Use a spade
to dig two trenches, 1 metre apart
and 30 cm wide and deep.

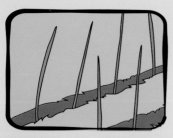

2 Plant the uprights. You will
need 13 willow stems for each
trench. Plant them about 30 cm
apart. Push each about 30 cm into
the ground. You might want an
adult to help you to do this if the
ground isn't very soft.

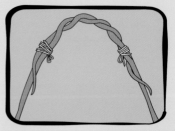

3 Bend each opposite pair of
willow stems to form an arch.
Twist them together. Fasten
with string. You now have the
main arch.

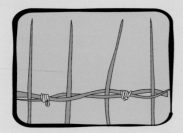

4 Now add the horizontals. Start at one end, about 15 cm up, and carefully weave a single stem through the uprights. Use a "behind, in front, behind, in front" type pattern. Use the rest of your rods to weave horizontally on both sides of the tunnel, spacing them equally. Secure them all with string.

5 Give the tunnel a good watering. Keep it well watered. In spring, the first shoots should appear.

DON'T FORGET
You need to make your tunnel when the willow rods are dormant – after leaf fall, and before leaf bud. After you've bought the willow stems, make a start as soon as you can.

6 You can either let your tunnel grow shaggy and wild or ask an adult to help you to neaten it up with garden shears. You should ask an adult to help you cut it back each autumn or winter with garden shears in either case. Never use shears on your own.

DONE! DATE COMPLETED

14 GET THE GOAL!

Ever dreamed of scoring goals like Cristiano Ronaldo? It'll take a bit of practise! Get your football career going in your garden or local park.

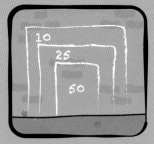

1 Chalk goalposts onto a wall at different heights and widths. Mark the scores onto the wall – write 10 points for the easiest, 50 points for the hardest, and so on.

2 Mark a kick line for you to place the ball. Aim at the goalposts to win the points. Chalk your points on the pavement.

REMEMBER
Don't forget to wash off the chalk marks afterwards – especially if you are using a public space.

3 After 10 kicks, add up your scores. How did you do? Take another 10 kicks, and see if you can beat your original score.

DONE!

DATE COMPLETED

THROW A MONSTER MURAL

15

You can just "throw" this one together. It's super-easy to create a super-size mural with just paint and play balls.

YOU WILL NEED:

- Large roll of paper or canvas
- Drawing pins or clothes pegs
- Dust sheet or old sheet
- Tempera paint
- Paint trays or disposable containers
- Textured play balls, for example, spike balls
- Permanent markers
- Googly eyes (optional)

1 Find a place to hang your paper or canvas. A shed wall or fence is ideal. Check with the owner that it's OK first, though. Canvases can also hang from a washing line. Spread out the dustsheet in front.

2 Squeeze different coloured paints into different containers. Roll a ball into one of the paints until it is covered. Stand about 1.5 metres from the paper and throw the ball.

3 Throw more and more balls until the paper is suitably splattered. You can "sign" it by dipping your hand into the paint and pressing it onto the corner of the paper.

4 Now get creative with the marker pens and googly eyes to make silly, serious, and seriously silly monster faces.

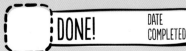

DONE!   DATE COMPLETED

16 DIG A DINOSAUR PARK

Ferns have been around since the dinosaurs roamed the earth, so it makes sense to use them to make your very own Jurassic Park. Let your imagination and the dinosaurs roam . . .

YOU WILL NEED:

- Toy dinosaurs
- Old car tyre (ask for an old one at an auto-repair shop)
- Outdoor paint
- Black rubbish bags
- Bag of compost
- Prehistoric-looking plants, for example, ferns
- Moss or garden gravel
- Rocks and pebbles

1 Wash the tyre. Make sure it's dry before painting the outside. To get a good, strong colour, you may need several coats. Let the paint dry between coats. Dry completely overnight.

2 Put the tyre in a shady spot where the ferns will grow well. Line the tyre with rubbish bags, making a few drainage holes in the bottom. Fill with compost.

3 Plant the ferns and water them. Add rocks and pebbles. You might want to pile up soil to make volcanoes, or add blue gravel as a lake. Cover the rest of the soil with moss or gravel.

DONE!   DATE COMPLETED

4 Now all you need to do is add the dinosaurs!

PLAY A BOTTLE XYLOPHONE

Become a music maestro with just a collection of old bottles, some water, and a good set of lungs. Glass bottles work best, but plastic will work too.

1 Place your bottles in a line about 5-10 cm apart. Pour a little water into the first bottle, a little more in the second, and so on, until all the bottles have a different amount of water.

2 Blow across the tops of each bottle one after the other to listen to the different pitches. To make a musical scale, place the bottles in order from the one that makes the lowest sound to the one that makes the highest sound. (You may need to remove water from or add water to some of the bottles.)

3 When you're happy with your scale, try to blow a simple tune that you know. See if you can "play" something you know well, such as, "Row, Row, Row Your Boat". Try another. Now make up your own song!

DONE!

DATE COMPLETED

18 SHOOT A BOW AND ARROW

Make mini bows and arrows, and perfect your aim. It'll take practise, but don't give up – even Katniss Everdeen had to start somewhere!

YOU WILL NEED:

- Craft sticks
- Cotton buds
- Dental floss
- Nail scissors
- Adult help

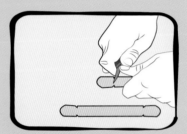

1 Ask an adult to carve notches into your craft sticks with the scissors. Working about 1 cm from the ends, you need a notch on each side, on both ends. You should have four notches on each stick.

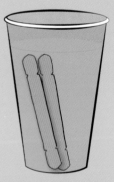

2 Put your sticks into a cup of warm water. Leave for at least an hour. This will soften the wood, allowing it to bend.

3 Remove the sticks from the water and dry them off. Wrap dental floss around one end of each stick about four times. Knot in place, leaving the rest of the floss to wrap around the other end of the stick.

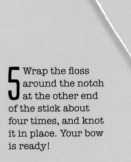

4 Holding the stick in one hand, stretch the dental floss to the notch on the other end. Make sure that you keep the floss on the same side. Carefully bend the stick as you stretch the floss tightly across it.

5 Wrap the floss around the notch at the other end of the stick about four times, and knot it in place. Your bow is ready!

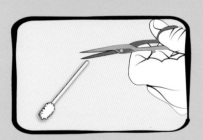

6 To make the arrows, simply snip one end off your cotton buds with nail scissors. Ask an adult to help you to do this.

7 Aim and FIRE! Line up rows of targets to practise on. They'll need to be small and light, such as toy figurines or pine cones. As you get better at hitting your targets, position them further and further away.

DONE! DATE COMPLETED

19 GROW POTATOES IN A BAG

Mashed potato, baked potato, chips? Yum! Get yourself some potatoes and get growing! If you can, you should "chit" your potatoes first – put them with the "eyes" facing upwards in an egg box for four to six weeks, and wait for them to sprout.

1 Take an old compost bag, and fill one-quarter of it with potting compost. Roll down the sides and carefully poke drainage holes into the bag with a knife. Keep the holes small so that you don't split the bag.

2 Put your potatoes on top with their "eyes" (the sprouted parts) up. Cover them with a little more compost, just to keep them in the dark. Water well and keep in a warm, sunny spot away from frost.

3 As green growth comes up, bury the foliage with more soil and roll a bit more of the bag up to accommodate. You'll need to do this every three to four weeks.

4 After 90 to 100 days, the potato plant will flower, and your crop will be ready to harvest. All you need to do now is tip the bag on its side (outside!) and shake out your potatoes. The only difficulty will be deciding how to cook them!

DONE!   DATE COMPLETED

MAKE POTATO PRINTS

Potatoes are great to print with, but you can use other homegrown or bought veggies too. Try halving peppers and cauliflowers, and experiment with celery leaves and carrot tops.

1 Cut a large potato in half and press a cookie cutter into the centre of the potato.

2 Ask an adult to slice around the cookie cutter. Remove the excess potato and the cookie cutter.

3 Squeeze the paint into the saucer and dip the potato into the paint. Press your potato shape onto the paper you want to decorate. Try doing this with your other vegetables too, and see what amazing artwork you can come up with!

DONE!

DATE COMPLETED

21 PUT ON A CLOTHESLINE ART SHOW

You don't need a huge space to set up an outdoor art studio – a balcony, patio, porch, or small lawn will do.

YOU WILL NEED:

- A clothesline or rope
- Pegs
- Paper
- Art materials
- Blanket and cushions (optional)

1 Set up your studio. It can be as simple as a pile of paper and a pot of coloured pencils on a rug. A few cushions might be nice too.

2 Be sure to ask an adult to help you to put up the washing line or tie a rope between two posts or trees. It should be at a height that you can reach. Put a bag or box of pegs near the line.

3 Ask a few friends to come and make some art. Pin your masterpieces to the line as you do them. Now invite more friends or your family to your art show.

DONE! DATE COMPLETED

RELAX WITH YOGA

Find a quiet spot in a garden, in the park, or at the beach, and try some of these basic yoga moves. Repeat them as many times as you feel comfortable.

1 Sit cross-legged. Raise one hand into a fist. Breathe in while counting to 5 and uncurling your fingers. Breathe out to the count of 5 while slowly curling your fingers back into your fist. Repeat on the other side.

2 Stand straight with your legs spread out and your arms at your sides. Breathe out and bring your right arm over your head while the left arm slides down your left leg. Repeat on the other side.

3 Stand straight with your hands together above your head. Breathe in deeply. Stare ahead. Breathe out, bending one leg slightly as the other comes up to rest the foot just below the knee of the standing leg. Hold as long as possible. Bring the bent leg down. Rest. Repeat.

4 Lie flat on the floor with your arms and legs stretched out. Breathe out and lift your arms and legs a couple of cm above the ground. Stay as long as you feel comfortable, then rest and try again.

DONE!

DATE COMPLETED

23 PLAY FROGS AND FLIES

Are any of your friends super sleuths? Maybe one or two are heading for a career on the stage? If so, they'll enjoy this game.

1 Sit in a circle and choose a detective. This person must now go away from the group, out of earshot, until he or she is called back. Now decide who is going to be the frog. Everyone else is a fly.

2 Call the detective back. The frog is going to "kill" the flies secretly while the detective isn't looking by sticking his or her tongue out at them.

3 The flies should "die" as dramatically as possible, with lots of spinning and buzzing. They eventually fall into a heap on the floor.

4 The detective needs to work out who the frog is before the flies are killed off. If the frog kills off all the flies but one, he or she wins. If the detective guesses who the frog is before that, he or she wins. But the detective only has 3 guesses.

5 For a new game, start all over again with a new detective.

WHY NOT?

If there's quite a large group of you, you could also select a fly saver. This is a person who can bring the flies back to life with a special signal (for example, pointing). But if the detective works out who the fly saver is, then he or she also becomes a dead fly.

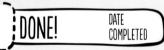

DONE!   DATE COMPLETED

24 THROW A SEEDBALL

"Throw it, grow it" is the seedballer's mantra. You can literally throw a garden into a place that needs a little bit of life and colour!

YOU WILL NEED:

- Seeds (easy-to-grow or native varieties)
- Clay (available from craft stores)
- Compost or potting soil
- Mixing bowl or bucket
- Spoon
- Water

1 Select seeds that are easy-to-grow without too much water or pampering. If you're mixing, choose plants that will look good together when they flower. Soak the seeds overnight and drain away the water in the morning.

2 It's best to mix your ingredients outdoors, as it can be quite messy. You need 5 cups of clay, 1 cup of compost, and 1 cup of seeds. Your cups can be as big or small as you like as long as you stick to these ratios – 5:1:1. Put the seeds and compost into your bowl and mix with the spoon.

3 Mix in the clay. Add water very slowly, drip by drip, and stir until you've bound everything together. The mixture should be moist, not dripping wet.

4 Knead the mixture with your hands. Take a handful of the mixture, and shape it into a ball – around the size of a golf ball. Use the rest of the mixture to make more balls.

5 Leave your seedballs to dry for a day or two. Then go to your chosen location, and . . . THROW! If they land on concrete or rock, don't worry – the seeds have everything they need to grow in the ball. Don't worry about watering either – nature will take care of that.

6 Return in a few weeks to check on your instant garden. Keep visiting to see it in full bloom.

IMPORTANT!

Make sure that you don't throw seedballs onto other people's property if you don't have their permission first. But if you think your neighbour, school, or local business has a patch of ground that could do with livening up, find out who's in charge and see if they'll play ball – "seedball", that is . . .

DONE! DATE COMPLETED

25 MAKE AN OUTDOOR PHOTO BOOTH

Don't be shy! Step right up! Everyone loves taking silly pictures. This simple booth will allow you and your friends to have hours of fun and lots of memorable snaps.

YOU WILL NEED:

- Large picture frame
- Fishing line
- A sturdy tree branch
- Dress-up clothes or props
- Mobile phone or camera

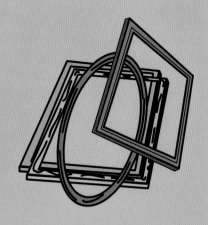

1 Find a large picture frame. It needs to be at least big enough to fit your head into. If you don't have something at home, hunt one down in a local charity shop.

2 Remove the backing and everything in the frame. You might need an adult to help you to do this. Repaint or decorate the frame if you want to.

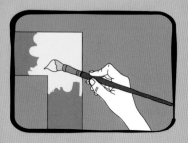

3 Find a tree with a sturdy branch in a nice setting for a photo. Ask an adult to help you to hang the frame from the branch with fishing line. You could also hang it from a post or hook.

4 Try out different heights and positions, for example, an oval frame might be nice on its side so that two people can fit into it. Make sure the frame isn't too high to reach! It needs to be at eye level.

5 Put a few props or an entire dress-up box on the ground near the frame.

6 Invite your friends over, ask them to stand behind the frame, and take their portrait! Encourage them to get inventive with the props.

DONE!

DATE COMPLETED

26 CLIMB A TREE

The world looks different from up here! Climb a tree and see everything from a new perspective. It's a pretty good hiding place too! Be sure to choose a dry day, as wet weather will make it much harder to climb.

1 Wear sturdy footwear to help you grip onto the bark, and long sleeves and trousers to protect you from scrapes and scratches. Find a big, sturdy tree with plenty of strong branches at regular intervals. Before climbing, do a few stretches to warm up.

2 Now stretch up to reach the first branch. Choose a branch that is at least as thick as your arm. Hold on to the branch tightly, test it to make sure that it will take your weight, and pull yourself up the trunk. As you climb up further, look for knots, bulges, crevices, and smaller branches to use as footholds.

3 Only climb up as far as you feel comfortable and safe. You can always climb higher next time! Take time to enjoy your view. Look around for animals living in the tree. Climb back down very carefully when you're ready to.

SAFETY FIRST!
Don't go too high up. Always take an adult with you. You might need help getting up or down the tree.

DONE!   DATE COMPLETED

CLOUD SHAPING

27

It's been said that clouds are the sky's imagination. Why not catch a little of its creative magic and try some cloud shaping?

1 Lie down on your back and stare into the sky. Watch the clouds drift by.

2 Let your mind wander. What do you see? Are there castles, horses, monsters . . .? Keep looking until you see something. Relax and just "be".

3 Now look at the blue spaces between the clouds. Pictures lie hidden there too.

TOP TIP
Cloud pictures don't just appear in blue summer skies. Try cloud shaping at sunrise and sunset and during a storm too.

DONE!   DATE COMPLETED

28 BUILD A BUCKET POND

You don't need a big space for a simple outdoor pond. You don't even need to dig a hole! Try this simple project, and wait for the wildlife to visit.

YOU WILL NEED:

- Watertight container, for example, an old bucket or baby bath
- Washed sand
- Washed pebbles
- Terracotta flowerpots
- Washed larger rocks and stones
- Water plants (available from garden centres – ask advice on the best ones to buy to oxygenate your pond)
- Rainwater

1 Find a container. You can use anything – from an old bucket or old-fashioned bathtub to an old baby bath or storage box – as long as it is watertight. It shouldn't be too deep so that creatures can get up to it easily. Wash it out thoroughly.

2 Pour washed sand into the bottom of your container until you've covered the base. Scatter pebbles over the sand. This will give the insects somewhere to bury and hide.

3 Put your flowerpots in upside down, then add the bigger rocks and stones. These will provide shelter for the wildlife.

4 Add some water plants. Check with the garden centre when you buy them that you're including good oxygenators.

5 Put in a shady spot so it doesn't overheat in the sun. Pile stones around the edge to help frogs and other creatures climb up. Place other plants nearby.

6 Fill up with rainwater. Don't use tap water – it has chemicals in it that might harm your pond life. Then just wait for your visitors!

DONE!   DATE COMPLETED

[29] HAVE A WATER CUP RACE

If you don't feel like getting soaked through with yet another water fight, use your water pistols for a cup race instead. All you need are plastic cups and string. Load . . . aim . . . go!

1 Ask an adult to help you make holes in the bottom of some plastic cups.

2 Set up a string line for each player by tying one end of each string to a post or a tree. Thread a cup onto the string before tying the other end. Make sure that each player's string is the same length – no cheating!

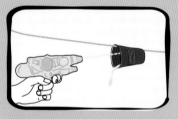

3 Pull the cups to equal starting positions. Place the bucket of water between each starting string line. Load your guns, and race your way to the finishing line!

WHY NOT?
Practise on your own using a stopwatch. What's your best time?

DONE!   DATE COMPLETED

INVITE YOUR FRIENDS TO A PICNIC

What better way to spend a gloriously sunny afternoon than with friends on a picnic? Plan ahead so you don't forget anything!

1 Decide on a lovely picnic spot – it might be in your local park, on the beach, or in your own garden. Then write invitations to your friends. Don't forget to say where, when, and what to bring.

2 Make a list of who's coming and the food to prepare. Think carefully about what everyone likes to eat. Sandwiches or wraps and fruit are good starting points. List items that your friends have promised to bring so that you can work out whether there will be enough to go round. An adult can help you to do this as well as to go shopping.

3 Set out with at least one friend, and make sure that an adult knows where you're going. Get there a little early so you're there before your other guests. Lay out the picnic blanket, eat, relax, talk, and throw a Frisbee! Don't forget to take all of your rubbish home with you.

WHY NOT?
Try a winter picnic with flasks of hot chocolate or soup. Wrap up warm, and take blankets to cosy up in!

DONE! DATE COMPLETED

31 MAKE A STICK FAMILY

When you're next in the park or the woods, try making your very own stick family. Add a few googly eyes and some other bits and pieces, and they'll really come to life.

YOU WILL NEED:

- Sticks (found on the ground)
- Thread or pipe cleaners
- Googly eyes
- Glue
- Marker pens
- Bits of fabric
- Scissors

1 Pick out your favourite sticks, and decide which to use for the bodies. Is there a cute little one for "baby"? Use thread or pipe cleaners to tie on smaller twigs for arms and legs.

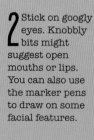

2 Stick on googly eyes. Knobbly bits might suggest open mouths or lips. You can also use the marker pens to draw on some facial features.

3 Wrap pieces of fabric around them for clothes. A ribbon tied under a "chin" makes for a good bow tie.

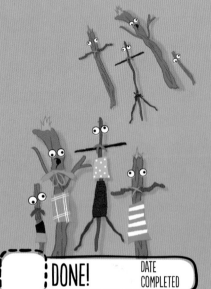

DONE!   DATE COMPLETED

FEED THE BIRDS

32

When food is hard to find in the winter, a peanut butter feeder will help to feed the local birds. If possible, hang it within view of your bedroom window.

1 Cut a length of string and tie it securely to the top of the pine cone.

2 Put the birdseed and any extras, such as sunflower seeds, corn, or nuts, into a bowl. Spread peanut butter all over the cone with a knife or spoon.

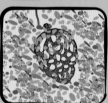

3 Dip the sticky cone into your bowl of seed. Roll it around until the peanut butter is completely covered with seed.

YOU WILL NEED:

- Pine cone
- Birdseed
- Peanut butter
- String
- Scissors
- Butter knife
- Thread or pipe cleaners

4 Ask an adult to help you to hang it from a tree branch or up high. Make sure that animals that like to eat birds can't reach it. Try to identify your visitors by looking them up in a birdwatching guide or on the Internet.

DONE! DATE COMPLETED

33 PLAY ELBOW TAG

You've probably played tag, but have you played this version? It's quite a challenge and best with a big group of friends in a large space.

YOU WILL NEED:

- A group of friends (at least 8, but the more the better!)
- Large area to run around in

1 Split into pairs. If there's anyone left over, have one group of three. Stand in your pairs with your elbows linked. Spread out in the play area.

2 Choose one pair to unlink elbows and become "It" and the Runner. Whoever is "It" chases the Runner. If the Runner is caught, he or she is tagged and will become "It". In turn, "It" will become the Runner.

3 To escape "It", the Runner can link elbows with one of the pairs to make a threesome. He or she is now safe. But the person at the other end of the threesome is now the Runner.

4 "It" must chase the new Runner. The new Runner can link onto a pair to pass on the role, but it must be a different pair from the one they were in before.

5 At any point, if "It" tags the Runner, the roles reverse. Play until you're all so exhausted that you fall down in a big heap!

WHY NOT?
Change the rules a little. You could speed-walk or hop instead of run.

DONE!

DATE COMPLETED

34 MAKE BARK AND LEAF RUBBINGS

Using paper and crayons, take rubbings of bark textures and leaf patterns, and start your own collection. Mount them in a scrapbook and use the Internet or a guide to identify them.

1 Place a piece of paper on the bark of a tree, and hold it in place with one hand. Rub a crayon smoothly across it, keeping all the strokes in one direction using the side of the crayon. The pattern of the bark and its ridges will be transferred to your paper.

2 Choose a leaf. It should be dry. Leaves that have lots of veins and ribs on them work best.

3 Place your leaf on a firm surface and put a strong piece of paper over it. Use your crayon in the same way that you did for the bark rubbing – keeping all the strokes in the same direction. One side of your leaf will be smoother than the other. Try rubbing both sides.

DONE!   DATE COMPLETED

THROW PAPER-PLATE FRISBEES

If you don't own a Frisbee, don't worry – it's very easy to make one with a couple of paper plates. So, how far can you throw it?

YOU WILL NEED:

- 2 paper plates
- Adhesive tape
- Scissors
- Marker pens

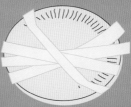

1 Cover one side of each plate with adhesive tape. Place the plates right side up, as if you're going to put food on them. Cover them with strips of adhesive tape, letting them overlap the edges.

2 Trim around the outer edge of each plate to remove the extra tape. Make a hole in the centre of one of the plates. Use a protractor or draw around a lid or a saucer to get a perfect circle. Pierce the centre of the circle with scissors to cut it out. Now cut a hole in the other plate in the same way.

3 Turn the plates over and decorate with marker pens. Now cover the decorated sides of your plates with tape. Let the tape hang over the sides, and trim it on one plate as before. Leave the overhanging tape on the other plate and use it to join the two plates together. Now you're ready to play!

DONE! DATE COMPLETED

36 SEND A SEMAPHORE

The semaphore flag system was designed more than 150 years ago, and it is still used today. Make yourself a semaphore flag and try signalling a message to your friends from the other side of a football field (or from the bottom of your garden).

YOU WILL NEED:

- 2 sheets of thick yellow paper
- 2 sheets of thick red paper
- Paper glue
- Ruler
- Pencil
- 2 dowels or flower sticks
- Adhesive tape
- Notebook and pen (for the person receiving your signals)

1 Draw a diagonal line from the top right-hand corner to the bottom left-hand corner of each yellow sheet of paper. Cut along the lines. Glue each triangle onto the backs and fronts of the red papers, making sure that the red triangles are always at the top.

2 Place the adhesive tape along the left-hand edge of each flag, half on the paper, half off.

3 Place the dowel over the tape, lining it up with the top of the flag. Flip over the flag and pull the tape tight, rolling the paper around the dowel as you go. Press hard to make sure that the tape sticks to the dowel and the paper.

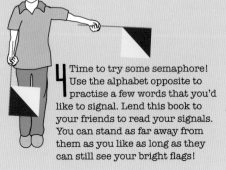

4 Time to try some semaphore! Use the alphabet opposite to practise a few words that you'd like to signal. Lend this book to your friends to read your signals. You can stand as far away from them as you like as long as they can still see your bright flags!

THE SEMAPHORE ALPHABET

DONE!

DATE COMPLETED

37 SKIP YOURSELF FIT

Skipping is a great workout. It's lots of fun too! If you haven't done it for a while, build up slowly.

1 Warm up gently with a slow Double Hop. This is when you skip with your feet together, turning the rope slowly. Jump twice between each rope turn. Try 10 of these.

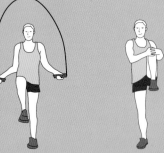

2 Next, do the Shuffle. This is when you put one foot in front of the other and switch feet as you skip. Jump twice between each rope swing. If you feel ready, try to speed it up with just one jump between each rope swing. Do 10 of these.

3 Now for the High Knee. Pick up one knee at a time while you skip. Again, start off by jumping twice between each rope swing. When you're ready, jump just once, as if you're running with your knees up high. Do 10 of these.

4 Time to cool down with some knee tucks. Take one knee in both hands and pull it up to your chest. Do the same with the other knee. Do again on both sides. If you're tired, go and rest. If you feel like you can do more, start back at step 1. Maybe try 15 of each this time instead of 10?

DONE!   DATE COMPLETED

MAKE DRIP CASTLES

You don't have to go to the beach to build these wild, magical towers – a sandbox will work just great!

YOU WILL NEED:

- A sandy beach or a tray of sand in your outdoor space
- A bucket

1 Prepare a solid base. If you're on the beach, pile up wet sand and flatten it. If you're at home, you could just work on a paving stone.

2 Half-fill your bucket with sand. Then fill to the top with water. Stir with your hand to get a gooey mix.

3 Collect a handful of your gooey sand mixture. Point your sand-filled hand thumb down. Then let some of the goo drip through your fingers. As the sand drips, it will build up into a stalactite structure.

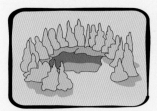

4 Keep dripping, moving your hand up and away from the tower as it gets taller. Group lots together, or build towers on top of towers to create one big one. Arrange in a circle for a ring of mountain peaks, or make a castle!

DONE! DATE COMPLETED

39 LAY A STICK TRAIL

Are you a good trailblazer? Head for the local woodland or park, and lay a trail for your friends to follow and find you. If there's a big group of you, split into Trailblazers and Trackers. The Trailblazers set the trail for the Trackers.

YOU WILL NEED:

- Bucket
- Sticks, stones, and other natural objects (found on the ground)
- A few friends

1 Gather together sticks, stones, pine cones, feathers, leaves, and any other natural objects you can find, and put them in your bucket. Don't pick anything from the trees – there will be plenty on the ground.

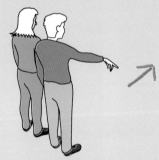

2 Decide on where your track will start and finish, and lay trails along the route. You can make up your own symbols, or use some of the examples on the opposite page.

SAFETY FIRST

Always tell your parents where you are going.

3 Now it's time for your friends to track you down. Use a few sticks to show them what to look out for and what your symbols mean. Ask them to count to 100 while you race to the end of your trail and hide. Can they follow your trail to find you?

GO STRAIGHT ON

TURN LEFT

TURN RIGHT

WRONG WAY

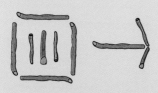

3 STEPS TO THE RIGHT

FOLLOW THE STREAM

GO OVER AN OBSTACLE

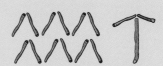

DONE!   DATE COMPLETED

40 PLAY BEANBAG LADDER TOSS

Are you better at throwing overarm or underarm? Can you throw blind? Practise your aim using just a step ladder, sheets of paper, coloured markers, and beanbags.

1 Write the scores onto different sheets of paper with coloured markers. You will need to write the scores: 10, 20, 30 (×2), 40, and 50. Make sure you draw the numbers big and bold so that you can see them easily.

2 Ask an adult to put up a step ladder in a large space outside. Tape the score papers onto the steps, with one of the 30 points sheets hanging from the bottom step, and then in ascending order (10, 20, 30, 40, 50) as you travel up the steps. Ask an adult to hold the ladder for you, and to help you to tape the scores onto the higher steps.

3 Now it's time to play! Either take turns with friends or play solo, trying to beat your best score each time. Your aim is to throw the beanbags between the steps of the ladder and win the number of points hanging above that hole. If your beanbag lands on a step, you lose 5 points.

DONE! DATE COMPLETED

MAKE A DAISY CHAIN

Flower power! Garlands, crowns, necklaces, bracelets, rings . . . you can make them all with these cute little flowers.

1 Find a daisy patch. Pick a few flowers with really long stems.

2 Use your thumbnail to carve a small slit into one daisy stem. (It's best to do this at the thickest part of the stem.)

3 Thread another daisy through the slit. Then make a slit in the stem of that daisy. Thread a daisy through that, and so on. Keep on going until your chain is the right length for your daisy jewellery.

4 To finish off, just make a slit in the last stem and thread the first daisy back through it. Wear your daisies with pride!

DONE!   DATE COMPLETED

42 LAUNCH A TOY PARACHUTE

Have you ever dreamed of making a parachute jump? Maybe you should let your toy action figure have a go first . . .

YOU WILL NEED:

- 25-cm square piece of lightweight fabric
- Scissors
- A button with 4 holes
- Two lengths of 90-cm thread
- Small plastic action figure

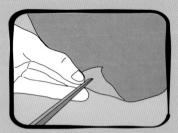

1 Fold over one corner of the fabric and snip a small hole with the scissors. Repeat on the other three sides.

2 Take one of your threads. Tie one end to the corner of the fabric.

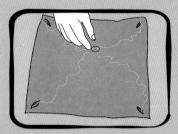

3 Take the other end of the thread through one button hole then through the diagonally opposite button hole.

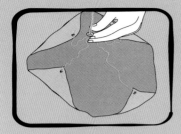

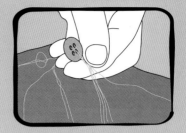

4 Pull the thread until the button is in the middle and tie the loose end to the opposite corner of the fabric. Repeat with the other thread and corners.

5 Hold the threads from the top of the button. Slide the button down about two-thirds of the thread and tie a knot.

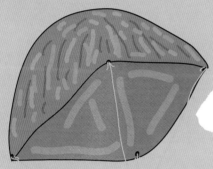

6 Tie the action figure to the end of the parachute. You're now ready for a test flight. Launch the parachute by throwing it in the air. Or drop it from a height (such as a wall, tree, or chair) with the help of an adult.

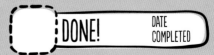

DONE!   DATE COMPLETED

43 CARVE A HALLOWEEN PUMPKIN

It's traditional to have a pumpkin lantern on your porch at Halloween. How scary can you make yours?

1 Ask an adult to cut off the crown (top) of the pumpkin with a sharp, serrated knife. Put the top to one side.

2 Scoop out the pumpkin flesh, pulp, and seeds with a spoon. (If you wash and dry the seeds, you can use them later to make art or jewellery.)

3 Use your marker pen to draw a spooky face. Make it as simple as possible. Ask an adult to use a small, serrated knife to cut out the eyes, nose, and mouth.

4 Put a tea light in the bottom of your pumpkin to light after dark. Pop on the lid, place on your doorstep, and ward away all evil!

DONE! DATE COMPLETED

MAKE A STRING TELEPHONE 44

The way that a string telephone works isn't so different from how an old-fashioned telephone worked, except that string is used instead of an electric current. Try different lengths of string to see how far away it will work.

YOU WILL NEED:

- 2 paper cups
- Non-stretchable thread (for example, kite string or fishing line)
- Measuring tape or ruler
- Sewing needle
- A friend

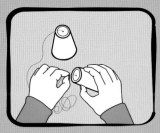

HOW DOES IT WORK?

When you talk into your cup, the bottom vibrates back and forth with sound waves. The vibrations travel along the string and are converted back into sound waves at the other end so your friend can hear what you said. Sound waves travel better through solids (such as your cup and string) than through air, letting you hear sounds that are much further away.

1 Cut a long length of string, between 20–30 metres long. Ask an adult to help you make holes in the bottom of your cups with a sewing needle. Thread the string through each cup and tie a knot at each end, inside the cups.

2 Take one of the cups each, and spread apart until the string is tight. One of you should talk into the cup while the other one listens. Can you hear what the other person is saying?

DONE!   DATE COMPLETED

45 BUILD A BOTTLE TOWER GARDEN

You don't need a big garden to grow vegetables and flowers. In fact, all you need to make this garden is a trellised wall or fence and lots of large plastic bottles!

YOU WILL NEED:

- Large plastic bottles with screw tops (2-litre soda bottles are perfect)
- Scissors
- An adult with a drill and a sharp knife
- Compost
- Handful of clean sand
- Seeds, seedlings, or small plants
- A trellised wall, fence, or freestanding trellis
- Garden twine
- Watering can

1 Clean the bottles and remove any labels. Ask an adult to help you to cut off the bottoms with a pair of sharp scissors.

2 Keep the lid on your first bottle. Ask an adult to help you make a small drainage hole at the top, at the bottle neck. Make another hole on the opposite side.

3 Fill the bottle with potting compost, leaving 2.5 cm at the top of the tower. Stand the bottle on the ground, lid down, next to the fence or wall to make the bottom of the tower.

4 Take the lid off your second bottle and fill it with compost. Place it on top of the first bottle. Use garden twine to secure the bottles to your fence or trellis.

5 Add a third, fourth, and even fifth bottle to your tower in the same way. The sixth bottle will be the funnel. It should have no soil and no lid. Cut it down a little more than the others and put it into the top bottle.

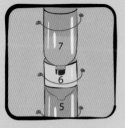

6 Bottle number 7 needs its lid. Ask an adult to drill a very small hole into the lid. Add a handful of sand to the bottle to filter the water. This is your filling-up bottle, which drops water through all of the other bottles.

7 Ask an adult to make windows in each bottle by cutting 3 lines into the plastic with a sharp knife. Pull down a rectangle of plastic. Push a hole into the compost and plant a seed, seedling, or small plant inside.

8 Keep your filling-up bottle well watered, and watch your garden grow!

DONE!   DATE COMPLETED

46 MAKE SUN PRINTS

Get creative with sun print papers. Special chemicals in the papers react to sunlight and help you to create awesome shadow prints. They're so cool, you'll want to hang them in your room!

YOU WILL NEED:

- Interesting-shaped objects, for example, toys, leaves, keys, etc.
- Sun print paper (available from toy stores and on the Internet)
- Tray
- Large plastic bowl of clean water
- Paper towels
- A sunny spot outdoors

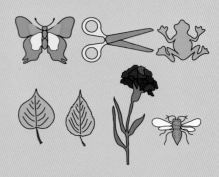

1 Find some fun-shaped objects. Small toys, plastic insects, leaves, keys, scissors, and flowers all work well.

2 Choose a shady spot, or do this part indoors, away from the window. Place a couple of sheets of sun print paper onto the tray. Make sure they don't overlap. Arrange your objects onto the papers.

3 Carry the tray to a sunny spot, taking care not to move the objects out of place. Leave the tray in the sunshine for 2 to 5 minutes. (If it's a little cloudy, leave for up to 20 minutes.)

4 Take a bowl of clean water out to the tray. When the sun paper has faded to white, take the objects off. Put the paper into the bowl. Leave it in the water for a few minutes. This is where the magic happens – the shapes of your objects will become white, and the faded blue background will become a dark blue colour.

5 Take your sun prints out of the water and rest them on some kitchen paper to dry. Impressed? Why not hang them in your room?

DONE!

DATE
COMPLETED

47 PLAY POOH STICKS

You can thank Winnie the Pooh for the invention of this super simple game. Pooh played it on a warm, sunny day with his friends. Play it with yours the next time you cross a bridge over a stream.

1 Each find a stick. Look at each other's sticks, and agree whose is whose. You could even tie a piece of different-coloured string to each stick to remind you which is yours.

2 Gather on the side of the bridge where the stream runs in (upstream). Stand side by side, holding your sticks at arms length over the stream.

3 Ready, Steady, GO! Drop your sticks at the same time.

4 Run to the other side of the bridge (downstream). Whoever's stick appears first wins!

DONE!   DATE COMPLETED

GO SLEDDING 48

There's nothing like zooming down the slopes on a sled, but make sure you do it safely. Wheee!

1 Wrap up warm, with a waterproof coat, trousers, gloves, hat, and boots. Wear lots of layers underneath to keep toasty and dry, but don't wear a scarf. Wear lip balm, and put some in your pocket to reapply. Put on your helmet.

2 Choose a good sledding hill: not too steep with a long flat area at the bottom, away from any roads and ponds, is perfect. It should be snowy rather than icy and free of obstacles such as rocks or trees.

3 Put your sled on the top of the hill. Sit on it facing forwards, with your arms and legs inside the sled, not dangling over the sides. Push off with your hands, and hold on tightly to the sides. If you fall off, move out of the way of your sled and any other sledders. If you can't stop, roll off the sled and get out of the way. GERONIMO! Time to go again? Walk back up the side of the hill, leaving the middle open for other sledders.

SAFETY FIRST
Always take an adult with you. Make sure that your sled can brake and steer. Practise braking before taking your sled on a hill, and only sled in the daytime.

 DONE! DATE COMPLETED

[49] GROW A BAG OF STRAWBERRIES

Instead of taking your shopping bag to the grocery shop to buy strawberries, fill it with compost and grow them instead! They're delicious with cream when they're ripe.

YOU WILL NEED:

- A sturdy reusable shopping bag
- Scissors
- 1 bag of potting compost
- 8 strawberry plants
- Broken eggshells
- Petroleum jelly

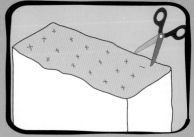

1 Ask an adult to help you cut drainage holes in the bottom of your shopping bag with the scissors. It's easiest to snip a hole, and then cut a cross shape.

2 Cut a horizontal slit about 5 cm across in the middle of the bag's front and back. Then cut two slits in the middle of each side of the bag.

3 Put your bag in a sunny, sheltered spot. It needs to be at least 30 cm above the ground, so you might want to rest it on a crate or small table. This will allow the plants to hang down without touching the ground.

4 Fill your bag with potting compost up to the level of the slits. Put 6 strawberry plants inside. Working from the inside, poke the leaves and crown (the part where the stems of the leaves meet in the middle) of each plant carefully through each slit. Spread the roots out in the bag.

5 Fill the bag almost to the top with the potting compost, and plant your remaining 2 plants at the top. Make sure that their roots are completely covered. Sprinkle broken eggshells onto the soil at the top (eggshells add calcium to your fertilizer) and smear petroleum jelly onto the sides of the bag to keep snails and slugs away.

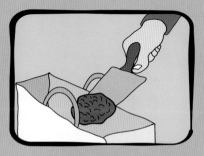

6 Water until the compost is evenly moist. Keep well watered. Every few days, rotate your bag so that all the plants get the same amount of sunshine. Then just wait for your strawberries to appear! After flowering, you should get ripe berries in just a couple of weeks. Don't be impatient – wait until they're red all over before picking the fruit.

DONE!   DATE COMPLETED

50 CREATE A SAND PALACE

Build a showstopping sandcastle fit for a king or queen. You'll need lots of wet sand and a bucketful of imagination!

YOU WILL NEED:

- Sandy beach
- Long shovel
- Dustbin with no bottom (an adult will need to cut off the bottom)
- A bucket or container with no bottom (an adult will need to cut off the bottom)
- Funnel
- Sculpting tools – whatever you can find at home. Cake decorating tools, spatulas, make-up brushes, craft sticks are all great.
- Spray bottle

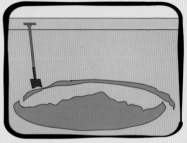

1 Find a good spot on the beach just above the tide line (where the dark sand becomes lighter). Use a long shovel to dig a circle in the sand, piling the sand up into the middle to make a hill. Don't forget to bend your knees!

2 Stamp the top of your hill into a volcano crater shape. Pour water into your crater. Use your feet to push down the sand. This will be the foundation for your sand palace.

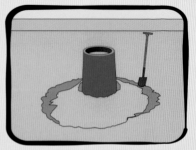

3 Now put your dustbin on top. Fill it three-quarters full with sand. Pour in a few buckets of water, and press down the sand with your hands or a bucket. Add more sand and water. Keep going until it is full.

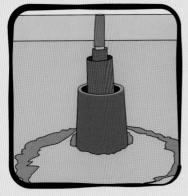

4 Add a slightly smaller bottomless container on top. Add sand until it's three-quarters full. Add water and push down, as in step 3. Continue to add and fill the smaller containers on top of one another.

5 Carefully pat the sides of the top container, and pull it off the top tower very slowly. Release all your containers from the top down.

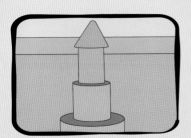

6 Add a turret. Fill the funnel with very wet sand, and put it on your top tower. Smooth the sand down. A make-up brush or spatula is good for this. You can add wet sand to finish off edges too.

7 And now for the detail. Always start carving from the top down so that the sand falls away from your finished areas. Keep the sand wet with your spray bottle. Join towers with spiralling ramps, using craft sticks to make steps. Cut archways, doorways, and windows . . . and don't forget to put flags on the top!

DONE!   DATE COMPLETED

51 FORECAST THE WEATHER WITH A PINE CONE

Pine cones naturally close when it is wet and open up when it is dry, so they are great weather indicators. Use one to make your very own weather-predicting hygroscope!

1 Cut off the top of a flexible straw at the top where it bends.

2 Position the tip of the straw on top of an open scale of the pine cone. Glue into place.

3 Put your pine cone onto a window ledge. When the air is humid, the scales of the pine cone will close and the straw will rise. This means that it is likely to rain. When it is sunny, the scales open up and the straw bends down.

DONE!   DATE COMPLETED

HAVE A TREASURE HUNT

Challenge friends and family to a treasure hunt around the back garden or in your local park. Don't forget to hide the "treasure" at the last clue!

YOU WILL NEED:

- 10–15 luggage labels with string
- Pen
- Adhesive tape
- Small prizes, for example, wrapped sweets (optional)
- Treasure prize

CLUES—APPLE TREE. BIKE. FRONT DOOR. BBQ. BACK DOOR. ROSE BUSH. BIRD FEEDER. SWING. GARDEN TABLE. PINE TREE
TREASURE — IN THE SHED

I GET HOT AND COOK SAUSAGES

1 Decide on where you're going to hide the treasure, how many clues there will be (10–15 works well), and where you're going to tie them. Write a list to help you remember.

2 Write the clues on the luggage labels. They might be pictures, e.g., draw an apple if the next clue can be found on the apple tree; descriptions, e.g., "I get hot and cook sausages" for the BBQ; or rhymes, e.g., "On me you can speed like a bird in the sky, my two wheels will make you fly!" for your bike.

3 If you want to, you could tape small prizes to the luggage labels, such as wrapped sweets. Tie the clues around the garden, always tying them to the next clue rather than the answer. Then hide the treasure.

4 Invite friends and family to hunt for the clues, removing them as they go – who will find the treasure first? You can help them if they get stuck, and if you're feeling super generous, have small consolation prizes for the losers.

DONE! DATE COMPLETED

53 THREAD A FLOWER GARLAND

In Hawaii, a flower garland is called a lei and is used to welcome visitors. Why not make your own to greet your friends?

YOU WILL NEED:

- Fresh flowers (with big receptacles – the thicker green part at the top of the stem)
- Scissors
- Strong thread
- Thick darning needle

1 Pick or buy the flowers that you'd like to use. If you're picking, check with the person who planted them first! You'll need about 40 flower heads for a full garland.

2 Cut the flower buds from the stem by snipping them at the bottom of the receptacle. Set the flowers aside, making sure that you don't crush the petals.

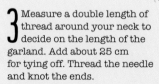

3 Measure a double length of thread around your neck to decide on the length of the garland. Add about 25 cm for tying off. Thread the needle and knot the ends.

4 Divide your flowers into two equal piles. For the first half, insert the needle through the flower from head to stem.

5 For the second half, insert the needle the other way around – from the stem through to the flower.

6 Push the flowers together on the thread. Then tie the garland into a circle by knotting the ends. Now greet your friends with a lei!

TOP TIP
Alternate the type and colour of flowers in the garland for a burst of colour.

DONE!   DATE COMPLETED

54 RIDE THE WAVES

If you've never been surfing, why not start with a boogie (or body) board? Just lie on top of the board and ride a wave to the beach. Surf's up!

YOU WILL NEED:

- Waves
- Sunblock
- Body board
- Leash
- Wetsuit (it needs to fit snugly but still allow movement)
- Booties
- Fins
  (A wetsuit, booties, and fins can all be hired with a body board)

1 Watch someone else boogie board first to get the idea. Then practise on the beach, using your feet and arms to paddle. This will give you a nice warm up, too.

2 Now it's time to get into the water! Make sure you're wearing your leash. Lie flat on your belly holding the side of the board with your hands. Keep your shoulders parallel to your hands, with your elbows bent, resting close to the outer edge of the board. Kick your feet, keeping them underwater.

SAFETY FIRST!

The beach can be very dangerous if you're not careful. Always take an adult with you, and do not try to boogie board unless you are a good swimmer. Always make sure that you don't go too far out so that you don't get caught in a strong ocean current.

3 Kick and paddle to where the waves are breaking. Choose the wave you want to ride, starting with a small one. A few seconds before the wave starts to break, point the nose of your board towards the beach.

4 Just as the wave reaches you, push off towards the shore. Let the board take your weight and lean up on your elbows with your head up and your back arched.

5 If you've caught the wave, it'll take you all the way to the beach. Was that fun? Time to go back in!

TOP TIP

Make sure that you have the right size board. They range from 90 to 115 cm long. Stand the board upright. It should come up to your belly button, or about 2 cm on either side of it. E.g., if you're 120 cm tall, then your body board would be 90 cm long.

DON'T PANIC!

If you fall off your board, don't worry – pull on your leash until you get hold of it again. Your board will keep you afloat.

DONE!   DATE COMPLETED

55 MAKE A BALLOON ROCKET

Real rockets need fuel to launch them into space, but you can send yours whizzing across the garden using just escaping air!

YOU WILL NEED:

- String
- Plastic drinking straw
- Balloon
- Masking tape
- 2 posts, trees, or hooks
  (at least 2.5 metres apart)

1 Tie one end of the string to a post or tree. Thread the loose end of the string through the straw. Pull the string tight before fixing it to the other post.

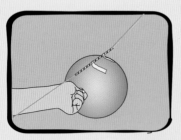

2 Blow up the balloon, but don't tie it off. Pinch the end and don't let go! Tape the balloon to the straw.

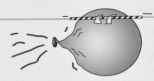

3 Pull the straw and balloon to one end of the string. Let go for blastoff! How quickly can it get to the end of the string?

DONE!   DATE COMPLETED

MAKE MUD FACES

After a rain shower, there's plenty of mud around. It's the perfect time to create a mud face. Will it be a beast or a beauty? A friend or a foe?

1 Dig up some mud and put it in a bucket. The stickier the mud is, the better. Add water to make it stickier if you need to.

2 Make a mud ball in your hands, and squash it onto the tree trunk, shaping it into a face.

3 Use natural materials to add features like eyes, teeth, a mouth, a nose, hair, and horns. Moss and fern leaves are perfect for shaggy hair, and pine cones are great for noses, horns, fangs, and eyes.

4 Name your beast, sprite, monster, or goddess, and leave it for someone else to find. When you go back, maybe another face will have appeared!

DONE!   DATE COMPLETED

57 MAKE TWINKLING LANTERNS

The flickering light of a lantern is all you need to enjoy your outdoor space after sundown. If you decorate it with magical creatures and tell imaginative stories, who knows what'll happen!

YOU WILL NEED:

- Old jam jar (or several)
- Acrylic paint pens
- 50 cm thin garden wire
- Beads
- Play sand
- Container with lid
- Food colouring
- Tea light (if possible, use Citronella to ward off mosquitoes and other biting insects)

1 Decorate your jam jar with acrylic paint pens. You could draw patterns and shapes or fairies, dragons, and other magical creatures. Leave to dry.

2 Now make the handle. Bend a loop at one end of the garden wire. Thread your beads from the other side until half the wire is covered.

3 Wrap the leftover wire around the neck of the jam jar, twisting the end to secure it.

4 Bend the beaded wire over the jam jar. Undo the loop you made in step 2, and thread this wire through the neck wire. Twist to secure, and tuck in any ends.

5 Take the lid off your container and put in a couple of spoonfuls of sand. Add a few drops of food colouring. Replace the lid and secure tightly. Shake for a minute.

6 Pour the sand into the bottom of your jam jar and add in a tea light. Hang your lantern up outside, ask an adult to help you light it up at twilight or use battery-operated tea lights. What sort of magic can you make happen?

DONE!

DATE
COMPLETED

58 PLAY HOPSCOTCH

It's thought this game began in ancient Roman times. Soldiers ran over courses 30 metres long in full armour to improve their footwork. Don't worry – yours can be much shorter, and you can wear anything you like!

YOU WILL NEED:

- Chalk (or a stone that leaves marks on a pavement)
- A small stone
- Pavement or area you can chalk on
- Any number of players – you can do this solo too

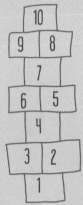

1 Draw a hopscotch course on the ground. Make sure the squares are big enough to fit one hopping foot!

2 Throw a stone to land on square 1. It mustn't bounce out or touch the border! If you don't get within the lines, you lose your turn and pass the stone to the next player.

3 If your stone lands in the first square, you can start your hopscotch. Hop over the first square, planting both feet on squares 2 and 3. Then hopscotch your way to number 10, hopping in single squares with one foot, and planting both feet on the side-by-side squares.

4 When you reach number 10, turn around on one foot and go back again. Don't forget to hop over square 1! If at any point you step on a line or lose balance, it's the next person's turn.

5 Now its time to throw your stone into square number 2. This time, you'll need to hop into squares 1, 3, and 4 before you plant both feet onto 5 and 6. Keep throwing your stone into the squares in order, and hopscotch your way through the course. You can just count up to 10, or do the countdown (from 9 to 1), too. Always hop over the squares with stones!

6 If you're really good, you'll finish the course before the next person even has a chance to take a turn, and you WIN! But it's more likely that you'll take turns until one person has finished.

WHY NOT?
Change the shape of the hopscotch course! You could try a spiral shape, or even try separating the boxes and jumping between them!

DON'T FORGET
to wash away your course at the end of the game.

DONE! DATE COMPLETED

[59] SAIL A LEAF BOAT

If you happen to be near a pond, stream, or lake, you can launch your leaf boat there. An upturned dustbin lid or wheelbarrow full of water will do just as well!

1 Collect your materials. You will need a "seaworthy" piece of bark, flat and broad enough to form the hull (the base) of your boat. If there's no bark on the ground, you could peel it away from a fallen, rotting tree trunk.

2 The bark may already have a hole in it, made by insect larvae. If not, make a small hole with a twig. (It helps if the bark is wet and softened.) Make the hole as central as possible, and push a twig into it, making sure it fits snugly. This will be your mast.

3 Thread a big leaf or series of leaves onto the stick for a sail. Find some water and launch your boat!

WHY NOT?

Add a passenger! Find a small pebble or flower head. Place it on the hull or on top of the mast, as if in a crow's nest. Will it stay aboard?

DONE!   DATE COMPLETED

TAKE LAVENDER CUTTINGS

Lavender smells lovely in your garden or on a windowsill. If you have a plant already, take cuttings in the summer, and you'll have more plants in the spring.

1 Choose a plant that is nice and healthy, with no pests or diseases. Look for a straight, healthy stem without any flower buds. Make sure that the stem is hard, not soft, and carefully cut it off with scissors. Remove the lower leaves so that the cutting has a bare stem.

2 Fill your pot with potting compost (first, mix it with grit if you have some). Push your cuttings into the side of the pot between the pot and the compost.

3 Water well and cover the pot with a plastic bag to keep it humid. Put it in a warm, shady place. Once the rooting has started, remove the plastic bag. When your cuttings are well rooted, move them into their own pots.

DONE!

DATE COMPLETED

61 MAKE AND PLAY PEBBLE DOMINOES

It's so tempting to collect those lovely smooth, flat stones on the beach or in the garden. But what do you do with them? With a little bit of paint and a steady hand, you can turn them into dominoes. This game has been popular since ancient times – a set was found in Tutankhamen's tomb!

YOU WILL NEED:

- 28 smooth, flat stones
- White paint pen (or acrylic paint, a small brush, and a steady hand)

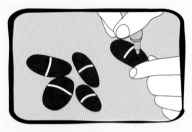

1 Collect 28 smooth, flat stones. Wash them to remove any sand or soil and paint a white line across the centre of each.

DOMINO PIECE GUIDE

2 Then, on either side of the lines, mark with two sets of dots in every combination from zero to six. Use this guide to make sure that you don't miss any.

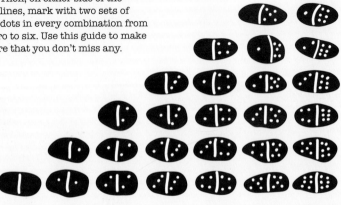

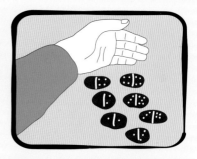

3 When the paint is dry, play with your dominoes on the lawn or at an outdoor table. You need at least one other player. First, place the dominoes facedown (with no dots showing) and shuffle them around. This is the boneyard. (This is because dominoes were originally made out of bone, or ivory. Yuck!)

4 Each player takes 7 dominoes. The players should see their own dominoes, but not the other players'. No peeking! Decide who starts by each picking up a domino from the boneyard. The player with the highest number of dots goes first.

5 Lay the first domino. The next player places one of his or her dominoes at one end of the first domino by matching the number of dots. If he or she can't go, then he or she should pick up a new pebble from the boneyard.

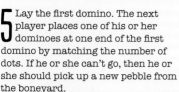

6 The game continues with each player matching one end of the domino chain in turn. If a double is laid, set the pebble vertically rather than horizontally. Every time you can't go, pick up from the boneyard. If you run out of space, start turning corners with the pieces. The first player to use up all his or her pebbles wins!

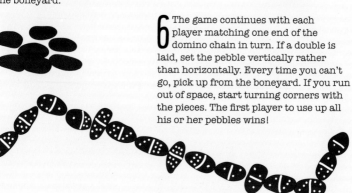

DONE!   DATE COMPLETED

62 PLAY WATER BALLOON DODGE

Cool off on a hot day, and invite your friends to a friendly water balloon fight. But be prepared to get wet – VERY wet!

1 Get your ammunition ready. Before filling up each balloon with water, blow it up and stretch it a little. This should stop it from popping. Stretch the neck of the balloon over the end of a tap or hose. Turn on a medium stream of water so that it doesn't shoot off! Turn the water off before the balloon is filled to the top.

2 Tie the balloons tightly, a few centimetres from the top. Put them in buckets. This can take a while, so ask your friends to help!

3 Select a referee and scorekeeper, and divide the rest of your friends into two teams. Agree on the rules before you start. When someone is hit, the other team scores a point. Will the teams take turns, or is it a free-for-all? Will you play until all the balloons are gone, until everyone has been hit, or when one team has reached a certain number of points?

DONE! DATE COMPLETED

GO HILL ROLLING

Want an exciting activity that is faster and more fun than walking? Try Mother Nature's very own roller coaster – go hill rolling!

1 Find a grassy hill. It needs to have a good slope, but make sure that it's not too steep. Make sure there are no rocks, litter, or animal droppings!

2 Empty your pockets and hand everything over to a friend. (It's pretty uncomfortable rolling over and over your things, plus you might lose something!)

3 Lay down on the ground at the top of the hill. Either cross your arms in front of you or put your arms above you.

4 And . . . roll! If there are other rollers, shout out "Wheeee!" so they know you're coming. Did you have fun? OK, so walk to the other side of the hill, get up to the top, and roll again and again!

SAFETY FIRST!
To be super-safe, wear a helmet and knee pads.

DONE! DATE COMPLETED

64 BUILD A WOODLAND DEN

If you go down to the woods today . . . why not build yourself a den? You don't need to take anything with you – all the materials will be in the woodland itself. A couple of friends would be a great help, though!

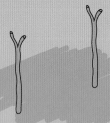

1 Find some open woodland to build your den. Look for a place with flat ground. Find two strong branches with forked ends for uprights. Drive them into the ground, a couple of metres apart, making sure they're at the same height.

2 Now you need to find a strong branch to sit across the forked uprights. This will be your ridge pole. Make sure that your structure is sturdy. If not, drive your uprights into the ground a little more.

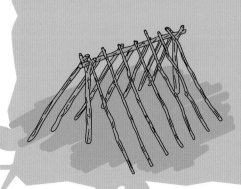

3 Gather up lots of strong, long sticks from the woodland floor. Only use dead wood – don't break any branches from the trees. Lean the sticks up against your ridge pole. Place them evenly on both sides. It's best to put a few on one side, then a few on the other, and so on, so that one side doesn't get too heavy and fall down.

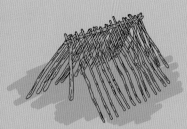

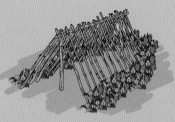

4 Continue to add sticks and branches until you have made a tent-shaped structure. Use as many sticks as possible to fill in the gaps. You can either close off one end in the same way, or leave both ends open.

5 Now you're going to thatch. Collect leaves from the forest floor, and pile them up against your structure. Start from the bottom, and work your way up. You can also use moss, pine needles, or bracken – anything you can find that is dead. Don't pull branches or leaves from the trees.

6 When you've finished thatching, go inside! It should be snug and warm in your woodland den – a perfect place to while away the hours with good friends.

DONE! | DATE COMPLETED

65 CATCH THE DRAGON TAIL

This is a traditional Chinese game inspired by the legendary Chinese dragon of ancient mythology. It's best played in a large group – perfect for a party! You need at least 10 people, but the more the merrier!

1 Choose a referee. Everyone else should make at least 3 teams. If possible, each team should have the same number of members. Line up the teams to face each other.

2 Tie or loop a scarf to the back of the last person in the line of each team. These are the dragon's tails. The people at the front of the lines are the dragons' heads. Everyone should hold onto the waist or shoulders of the person in front of them.

3 When the referee shouts "Catch the dragon tail", the game begins. The dragon heads need to get the scarves, or tails, from the other teams. The team lines must not break, and no one but the dragon heads are allowed to catch the tails.

4 When a tail is caught, the head shouts "caught" and the referee awards the team a point. If a line is broken or anyone but the heads catches the tail, the team loses a point. The referee needs to write down the scores.

5 The scarf is given back to the "tail", and the game continues. You can either play for a set amount of time or until one team has reached 5 points. The team with the most points is the winner!

DONE! DATE COMPLETED

66 MAKE A GEYSER

If you like messy, dramatic experiments, this is one for you! With just a bottle of diet cola and a packet of Mentos sweets, you can create a mighty geyser. Some people say theirs have been 8.8 metres tall! How high can you make yours?

1 Find an open space where you can make a mess. Go as far away as possible from anyone's nice clean windows or anything else you don't want to get sticky and yucky!

2 Stand the bottle of cola upright and unscrew the lid. If you have a funnel, put it into the top of the bottle.

3 Drop about half a packet of Mentos into the bottle through the funnel, and get out of the way! Stand far back to watch a mighty, bubbly geyser erupt from the bottle!

DONE!   DATE COMPLETED

GO ON A NATURE HUNT 67

Get together with a couple of friends and challenge them to a nature hunt. Decide as a group what to look for and what to do with your treasures at the end.

IDEAS LIST

Things that are:
Round, fuzzy, green, hard, soft, beautiful, red, orange, light, heavy

Something you can: Fly, spin, twirl, make a noise with

Make something from:
A pine cone, 3 different leaves, 5 seeds, a flower, a berry, a feather

1 Make sure that each hunter has a grocery bag, a pen, and some paper. Sit and agree on a list of things to look for. As you agree on an item to hunt, write it down. You'll each need a copy of the list.

2 Agree on where you'll go – perhaps in your back garden or in the park. Make sure that an adult always knows where you are.

3 Find every item on the list and put it in your bag. Do not pick flowers or leaves – try to find them on the ground.

4 When you've finished, make sure that everyone else has too. Take your stuff home to compare – you can make a little exhibition with the best finds.

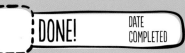

DONE! | DATE COMPLETED

68 SKETCH A TREE

Do you have a favourite tree in your garden or on your way to school? Why not capture it on paper? It's easy if you focus on one part at a time.

1 Sit down in front of your favourite tree, and get comfy. Look carefully at its overall shape, trunk, branches, and leaves. You're going to start drawing it from the bottom and work your way up. Draw the sides of the tree trunk and any roots at the base of the tree.

2 Now draw the main branches. Notice how they get thinner as they spread out. Allow some branches to be behind others. Include the unusual shapes that branches often make.

3 Draw the bark patterns on the trunk and branches. Add as much detail as possible. Shadows and lines will make it more realistic.

4 Draw the smaller branches and twigs. Notice how the smaller twigs branch off the larger ones, and even smaller twigs branch off of those.

5 Now add some softer marks for the leaves. You don't need to draw every leaf on its own.

6 Take a look at where the shadow falls on your tree. Start with the trunk, and add shade and tone. Now shade the branches that fall into shadow. Shade the leaves last. When you've finished, don't forget to sign your masterpiece!

DONE!

DATE COMPLETED

[69] TOAST MARSHMALLOWS

Whether you're sitting around a fire on the beach at night, snuggling around a campfire in the woods, or just having a barbecue, it's the perfect time to toast some marshmallows – YUMMY!

1 Poke a marshmallow onto a stick. Make sure that the end of the stick goes through the other end of the marshmallow so that it won't slip off into the fire.

2 Put the marshmallow over (not in) the fire or hot barbecue coals. Rotate the stick to cook it evenly. If you like your marshmallow gooey, take it away from the fire as soon as it's puffed up, or wait until it turns a golden brown colour on the outside.

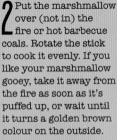

3 Remove the marshmallow from the fire. Let it cool for a minute. Then bite off the marshmallow from its stick and let it melt in your mouth. Delicious! Time for another?

WHY NOT?
Add toppings? Dip your toasted marshmallows into chocolate or caramel sauce, and then cover in chopped nuts!

SAFETY FIRST
Never light a fire without an adult. If your marshmallow catches fire, blow it out, don't shake it.

DONE! DATE COMPLETED

USE NATURAL DYES

Try out nature's very own dyes. Experiment with different leaves, berries, and vegetables to see which colours you can make and which work best.

YOU WILL NEED:

- Salt
- Light-coloured old T-shirt or scarf
- An old saucepan
- Knife
- Spoon
- Plants, fruits, or vegetables (like blueberries, carrots, and beetroot)
- Rubber gloves
- Sieve

1 Pick the vegetables or berries that you want to use. Ask an adult to help you chop them up. Put them in an old saucepan, and then half-fill it with water. Ask an adult to bring it to the boil, simmer for about an hour, and strain.

2 Adding salt and cold water will help the dye stay on the fabric. Add half a cup of salt to every 8 cups of water. Soak your T-shirt in the fixative (the salt and water) for about an hour. Rinse your T-shirt in cool water until it runs clear.

3 Wearing gloves, put your T-shirt into the dye. Press it down until it's completely covered. Leave overnight. Wearing gloves, remove it from the pan, wring it out, and hang it up to dry.

DONE!

DATE COMPLETED

71 BUILD A SNOW PENGUIN

I bet you've built a snowman, but how about a
snow penguin? It can look very cute in all that
amazing snowfall and is actually based on the
traditional snowman shape.

1 Wrap up warm, and don't forget
your gloves! (In fact, take a
spare pair or two for when they
get wet.) First, make the base. Roll
a large ball of snow, just as you
would for building a snowman.
Leave it where you want your
penguin, with the flattest side up.

2 Roll another ball of snow that is
about two-thirds the size of the
first ball. Put it on top of your
base. Now make one more ball of
snow that is about half the size
of the second one. It should be as
round as possible. Put it on top.

3 Fill the gaps between the
snowballs with more snow.
Smooth and pat the snow
down. Keep adding more snow
and smoothing it down until you
have a pear-shaped "body".

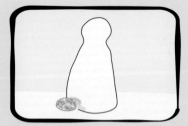

4 Gather snow around the base,
and shape it into two feet. Use
your fingers or a stick to make
gaps between the "claws" so the feet
look webbed.

5 Now add the penguin's wings. Draw a wing shape on each side with your finger. Carve out the shape so the groove is clear, and then add snow. Pat and shape the snow to fill out the wings.

6 The beak is the most delicate bit, so don't worry if it takes a few tries. It's easiest to have a stick support to build around. Find a stick that's a little longer than the length you'd like for your beak, and stick it into your penguin's head. Pack snow around the beak and shape it into a beak shape as you go.

7 And lastly, the tail! Gather up snow to form a tail shape directly from the penguin's base on the snow. Now the body is finished! If you spray your penguin lightly with water from a spray bottle or hose, it will freeze solid and last longer.

8 Now add eyes with small stones and maybe a hat and a scarf for fun! Don't forget to take a photo!

DONE! DATE COMPLETED

72 SPIN A PICTURE

Watch out for flying paint! You should wear old clothes that you don't mind getting dirty for this project. If you don't know Damien Hirst's spin paintings, look them up on the Internet, and see if yours match up.

YOU WILL NEED:

- Paper plate
- Adhesive tape
- Drawing pin
- Small amount of modelling clay
- Shallow box (big enough for the plate to sit inside with space around the sides)
- Poster paint
- Thick paintbrush

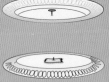

1 Stick some tape onto the back of the plate, in the middle. Push the drawing pin through the centre of the other side of the plate, through the tape.

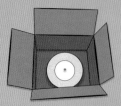

2 Put the modelling clay into the middle of the bottom of the box. Push the plate onto the clay blob with the drawing pin. Try spinning the plate. Adjust it up or down to spin as smoothly as possible.

3 Take some paint onto your brush and drip it onto the plate, spinning the plate at the same time. Add as many colours as you like, but keep spinning! When you have a spin picture that you like, let it dry. Then make enough to make a spin picture gallery.

TOP TIP

If you have a salad spinner, you could use that! Just put your plate inside, drip on the paint, and spin!

DONE!   DATE COMPLETED

PLAY RED LIGHT, GREEN LIGHT

Can you react quickly and stay as still as a statue? Grab some friends, find a big playing area, and give it a try!

1 Decide who is going to be the "traffic light". He or she stands at one end of the playing field. All of the other players stand behind a line at the other end of the playing field facing the "light".

2 The "light" turns away from the other players. When he or she says GREEN LIGHT, the players run towards the "light". When the "light" says RED LIGHT, he or she turns around and the players must freeze.

3 If players wobble or fall, they are sent back to the starting line.

4 The goal is to tag the "light" on the shoulder and become the "light" yourself. The "light" needs to try to trick the other players into wobbling or falling by turning around suddenly and quickly.

DONE! DATE COMPLETED

74 MAKE RANGOLI PATTERNS

Swirling bright colours in intricate patterns are laid on doorsteps and courtyards in India during the festival of lights – Diwali. They are called rangoli, and they welcome guests into people's homes.

YOU WILL NEED:

- Table salt (the more you have, the bigger your design)
- Runny paints (craft/poster/ tempura paint) in 3 different colours (you can use whatever 3 colours you like)
- Bowl
- Spoon
- Doorstep, paved area, patio, or driveway outside your home

1 Pour one-third of your table salt into a bowl. Add a spoonful of one of your runny paints and stir until it has mixed into the salt evenly. Add more paint if you want a stronger colour. Make the other two colours with the rest of the salt, then leave to dry out overnight.

2 Find a place to display your rangoli. It is traditional to put it near the entrance to your home, so maybe on your driveway, pavement, patio, or courtyard. Make sure that it won't get in anyone's way. Sweep the area first so you have a clean surface.

3 Take a handful of the first coloured salt, and place it in the centre of your chosen space. Shape it into a circle.

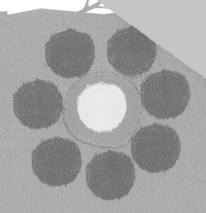

4 Take a little of the next coloured salt in the palm of your hand. Use your thumb and forefinger to sprinkle it neatly around the edge of your circle. Neaten it with the tips of your fingers.

5 Take a handful of the last coloured salt, and place it above the circle. Add another 6 handfuls, and round them off to become petals.

6 Use the rest of your first coloured salt to create a frame around the petals.

7 Add handfuls of salt to the dips in the flower's frame, and shape to finish off. You can add night lights around your rangoli pattern to make it especially welcoming. When you want to make a different design, simply sweep the salt away and start all over again!

DONE!   DATE COMPLETED

SPRAY-PAINT STATIONERY

Personalize your stationery with spray paint and found objects. You can create all sorts of patterns and textures for that special thank-you note, birthday card, or wrapping paper.

YOU WILL NEED:

- Empty spray bottles
- Paint
- Water
- Thick paper or blank writing paper
- Newspaper
- Found objects (leaves, pebbles, shells, feathers, recycled materials)

1 Wash the spray bottles out thoroughly. Squeeze the coloured paints into different bottles and add water. They shouldn't be too runny. Spray some onto some old newspaper to check the consistency.

2 Lay the newspaper on the lawn or patio, and put your blank paper on top. Arrange collected objects such as pebbles, leaves, feathers, or other interestingly shaped recycled materials onto the paper.

3 Spray the paint mixture over the paper and objects. Leave to dry, and then remove the objects carefully to reveal your spray-paint patterns.

DONE!

DATE COMPLETED

TAKE YOUR CAMERA FOR A WALK

When you walk to school or go shopping, do you really notice everything that's around you? If you take your camera for a walk, you might just start to see everything in a brand new light.

1 Decide on a walk. It might be a routine journey to school or the walk to a friend's house. It could be somewhere new, for example, when you're on holiday. Always let an adult know where you're going.

2 As you walk, keep your eyes peeled for great photo opportunities. What catches your eye? Is there something you always look out for? Do you meet the neighbourhood cat? Is there anything funny?

3 It's always exciting to look at the pictures you've taken. You could print them out, order, and write on them or make a slide show on your computer. Share them with your friends and family, and ask them to guess where they were taken.

DONE!

DATE COMPLETED

MAKE YOUR OWN HAMMOCK

Have a lazy outdoor day, gently swinging in a hammock. If you don't already have one, make your own! All you need is a sheet, some climbing rope, and an adult to hang it up for you.

YOU WILL NEED:

- 1 large bed sheet (not too old and worn)
- 2 pieces of 60-cm utility cord (available from climbing shops and hardware stores)
- 2 pieces of 1-metre webbing (available from climbing shops and hardware stores)
- Adult help

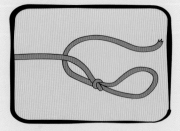

1 Take one piece of cord and make a loop at the end. Secure with a double knot. Leave a 10-cm "tail".

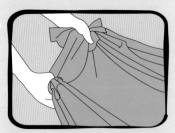

2 Loosely zigzag fold or gather your sheet lengthways. Then fold over one of the width ends at about 20 cm.

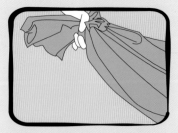

3 Gather the fabric from both sides about 10 cm in from the edge. Hold with your fist.

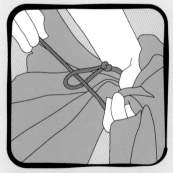

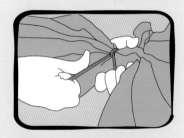

4 Wrap the cord around the sheet where your fist is, and then thread the cord through the loop.

5 Pull the cord until the loop is tight to the sheet. Wrap the cord tightly around the sheet 5 or 6 times, and tie the two ends together with a secure double knot.

6 Thread one piece of webbing through the end of your sheet. Tie a secure knot in your webbing. Repeat these steps on the other side.

7 Your hammock is now ready for an adult to hang up for you. Ask him or her to check that your knots are secure first, and to tighten them if necessary.

DONE! DATE COMPLETED

78 RACE MINI JUNK RAFTS

Get creative with recycled rubbish, and build the ultimate mini raft. Get your friends to make one too, and race them in the park on a breezy day.

YOU WILL NEED:

- Recycled and found bits and pieces – plastic trays and bottles, straws, corks, bamboo, craft sticks, bottle tops, twigs, pine cones, feathers, etc.
- String or rubber bands
- Inventive and competitive friends!

1 Gather lots of useful stuff. Think about whether they will float. Cardboard will soak and sink, but an old flat cheese grater might stay above the water if fixed to a couple of plastic bottles. Combine man-made and natural materials. Be inventive, and think outside the box!

2 Decide on your raft's shape. It doesn't have to be square. Lay the materials out and arrange them. Fix the pieces together with string or rubber bands, or both.

3 Name your raft and challenge your friends to a race. A breezy day on a shallow pond in the local park is perfect. But make sure that it is safe to wade in afterwards to retrieve your inventions!

DONE! DATE COMPLETED

TRY STONE SKIMMING

When you visit the seaside, a lake, or a river, try to beat the stone skimming record of 51 bounces. It takes practice, but if at first you don't succeed, try, try again!

1 Find a flat stretch of water with a good supply of rocks. Look for a skinny, flat, oval rock about the size of your palm.

2 Hold the stone between your thumb and forefinger in your strongest hand. Imagine the rock's path, choosing a spot ahead of you where you want the first bounce to be. Angle your hand so the front of the stone is pointing slightly upwards.

3 Keep your elbow close to your body and swing out from your hip. Swing your arm in an arc. As your arm reaches the bottom of the arc, straighten it and flick your wrist to release the stone.

TOP TIP

The smoother and flatter the stone, the better it will skip across the surface of the water without breaking the surface tension.

DONE!

DATE COMPLETED

[80] PRESS FLOWERS

Keep summer alive forever! Pressed flowers are perfect for framing, decorating, or even placing inside a locket. There are lots of ways to press them, but here is the simplest way.

1 Find a heavy book. Encyclopedias or dictionaries are ideal. The moisture from the flowers might wrinkle the pages, so make sure the book isn't precious to someone!

2 Lay the book open somewhere near the middle. Line it with two sheets of paper on either side. Cut the paper to fit if you need to. The outer two sheets are your "blotters".

3 For best results, pick your flowers when they're at the height of their bloom, when their colour is at its brightest. Choose flowers with fresh petals that haven't started to droop or die and that aren't damaged by insects.

4 Ideally, pick flowers when they are dry. But if you pick flowers that are still wet with dew or rain, allow them to dry completely before you press them. Dab them gently with kitchen paper to speed up the drying process.

5 Lay your flowers on one side of the book. Arrange them with spaces in between, and not too close to the paper edge. Do not overlap, unless you want your finished pressed flowers to do so.

6 To press flowers with a conical shape (like tulips or roses), cut them in half lengthways, or press individual petals.

7 If you have a lot of flowers, line other pages of your book with four sheets of paper, and use those too. But make sure that you leave about a centimetre between the different pages that you're using to press the flowers.

8 Close the book very carefully, without disturbing your flower arrangement or the paper alignment. Pile more heavy books on top of the pressing book. Leave in a dry place in your home.

9 Change the paper sheets every few days. Do this very carefully so you don't disturb the delicate flowers. After a couple of weeks, the flowers will be completely dry. Remove carefully with your fingers or a pair of tweezers.

DONE! DATE COMPLETED

81 MAKE A COLANDER WIND CHIME

You can't beat the soft jingle of a wind chime blowing in the breeze. You can use all sorts of bits and pieces to make one. Use your imagination!

YOU WILL NEED:

- Fishing line (ideally) or string
- An old colander (or any other plastic or metal object with holes, for example, a cheese grater)
- Bits and pieces that you can thread or tie, such as beads, keys, shells, buttons, pine cones, paper clips – whatever you like!

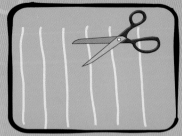

1 Measure and cut six pieces of fishing line, about 75 cm long. Gather together all of your found bits and pieces.

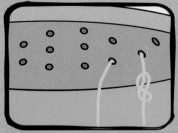

2 Thread one piece of fishing line through two holes just above the circular rim of your colander. Pull through until you have half the length hanging from each hole. Tie knots in the middle of the fishing line to fix it securely. The two threads should dangle down.

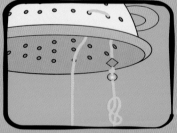

3 Thread or tie your treasures onto each side of the fishing line, one at a time. Each time you slide a bead or button onto the string, tie a knot beneath it. Make sure that the knot is big enough to stop them from sliding down.

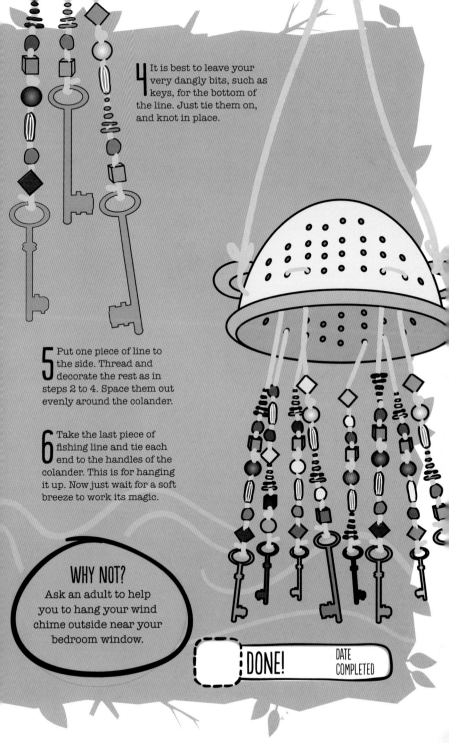

4 It is best to leave your very dangly bits, such as keys, for the bottom of the line. Just tie them on, and knot in place.

5 Put one piece of line to the side. Thread and decorate the rest as in steps 2 to 4. Space them out evenly around the colander.

6 Take the last piece of fishing line and tie each end to the handles of the colander. This is for hanging it up. Now just wait for a soft breeze to work its magic.

WHY NOT?
Ask an adult to help you to hang your wind chime outside near your bedroom window.

DONE!   DATE COMPLETED

82 MAKE ANGELS IN THE SNOW

Here's how to make perfect angels in the snow. If you go out right after a snowfall, you'll have a blank canvas to work on.

1 Find a patch of snow that's at least as tall as your body and as wide as your outstretched arms. Fresh powdery snow is best, so if possible, do this immediately after snowfall. Carefully fall back onto the snow with your arms outstretched.

2 Move your arms and legs back and forth, keeping them straight as if you're doing a jumping jack. Press your head back hard enough to make sure that you're leaving a good imprint.

3 Get up carefully so you don't spoil your masterpiece. If a friend is with you, ask him or her to help you up. Stand back and admire your snow angel. Take a photo!

DONE!   DATE COMPLETED

WIN AN EGG AND SPOON RACE

83

Have you ever been in an egg and spoon race? Gather a few friends to race against, or compete against the clock to become an egg-spert!

1 Cook the eggs in boiling water for about 8 minutes so that they're hard. Let them cool down before you use them. Its best to have an adult around for this step!

YOU WILL NEED:

- Enough eggs for each of your competitors
- Spoons to balance the eggs on
- Sticks and/or ropes
- An adult to help you

2 Decide on your racecourse, and mark the start and finish lines with ropes or sticks. Pick out a spoon that's big enough to fit your egg on it but not so big that the egg rolls around.

3 Hold one arm out in front of you with the egg and spoon almost at eye height. Keep your head and arm as still as you possibly can while running as smoothly as you can. Avoid any sudden movements! Keep your eye on the finish line, and try not to drop your egg. If you drop your egg, you must go back to the beginning!

DONE!

DATE COMPLETED

84 BUILD A SPUDZOOKA

Air pressure can be extremely powerful. It's even been used to launch satellites into space! This potato cannon (or spudzooka) uses the power of pressure to send potato pieces a long way!

YOU WILL NEED:

- A length of copper piping, 30–60 cm
- Dowel or garden cane
- Large raw potato
- Metal nail file
- An adult to help you

SAFETY FIRST!

Never fire your spudzooka at people or animals. Do this with an adult. You must always be outdoors in a large space.

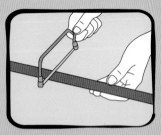

1 Find a length of copper piping. If you don't have any, ask for an offcut at your local hardware store. They may cut it to size for you, too. Otherwise, ask an adult to cut it to between 30 and 60 cm long.

2 Make sure that the pipe is straight and that the ends are smooth. If there are any rough edges, ask an adult to file them down for you. Do not touch the ends before they are filed down, as they may cut you.

3 Time to "load" your spudzooka. Put the potato onto a table (make sure you protect the table first) and hold it with one hand. With the other hand, push one end of the pipe all the way through the potato.

4 Push the other end of the pipe through the potato in the same way as before. Take the pipe out. Now you should have potato in both ends of the piping.

5 Line the pipe up and aim at a target. Poke one end of your spudzooka with the dowel and keep poking until it "fires".

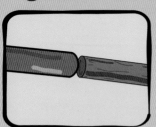

6 To use your spudzooka again, push out the potato that's still there with your dowel, and reload, as in steps 3 and 4.

WHY NOT?
Make a target for your spudzooka. Dip the end of the potato in paint so you can see where it hits. Bull's-eye!

DONE!   DATE COMPLETED

85 CREATE YOUR OWN WALK OF FAME

Since the 1920s, famous movie stars have left their handprints in paving stones on Hollywood Boulevard. It's part of the Walk of Fame. Why not recreate it in your own back garden, but this time, you and your family are the stars?

YOU WILL NEED:

- A disposable container (for example, plastic plant dish or even a sturdy cardboard box will do)
- Disposable plastic gloves
- Bucket
- Powdered cement mix
- Vegetable oil and brush
- Trowel or putty knife
- Stick or pencil
- Small toys, trinkets, or glass pebbles

1 Put on your gloves, and then mix the powdered cement and water in the bucket according to the instructions on the packet. It should become a thick paste.

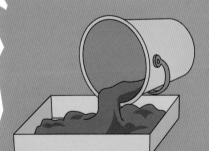

2 Brush a little bit of vegetable oil into the base of your container. Pour in the cement and smooth the top with the trowel. Let it sit for about an hour.

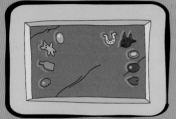

3 Leave a space that will be large enough for your handprints. Decorate the rest with your trinkets and pebbles. Try to use objects that say something about you. For example, an old but special toy car or something that is your favourite colour.

4 Use the stick to write your name or initials. You could also add the date. Remove your gloves, spread out your fingers, and press firmly to make a print in the cement. Wash your hands thoroughly immediately after.

5 Let the stone sit for a few days before getting it out of its container.

6 When you've made a stone with each member of the family, lay them out on your lawn or backyard, and celebrate with an opening ceremony!

SAFETY FIRST!
Wash your hands thoroughly with soap and water as soon as you've made your handprints in the cement.

DONE!   DATE COMPLETED

86 BUILD A BUG HOTEL

Bugs are great for the garden, and they're fascinating too. Make a "hotel" for them to shelter in during the cold winter months, and see who checks in. But be patient! It might take several months before your visitors decide to stay.

1 Get some large, plastic soda bottles and remove any labels. Ask an adult to help you to cut off the bottoms with a pair of sharp scissors. Keep the tops screwed on.

2 Line each bottle with corrugated card. This will make it dark inside the bottle.

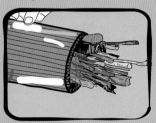

3 Fill each bottle with nesting materials like straw, dry leaves, small twigs, moss, and bark. Pack them in as tightly as possible so they don't fall out.

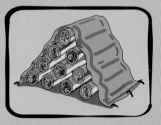

4 Stack the bottles into a pyramid shape, and cover them with felting or plastic. Weigh the "roof" down with logs or tent pegs so that it doesn't blow away. Check your hotel regularly to make sure that it's intact as well as to spot the visitors!

DONE!   DATE COMPLETED

GO ROCK POOLING

87

Rock pools are great little open-air aquariums.
When you're at the seaside, pick up a bucket and
take a look!

1 Before you set out, get a
bucket and a net, and make
sure that you've checked
the tide times carefully. Stay
away from any cliffs. Put
a little seawater into your
bucket, and start hunting!

2 Think like a marine creature
– they like shady, protected
spots, so look under rocks,
among seaweed, and between
cracks in the rocks. Carefully
dig with your fingers to see
what you can find.

3 Pick up creatures
carefully and put them in
your bucket or container
for a closer look. Some may
be very small or camouflaged
against the sand or weeds.
Always put creatures back
where you found them, and
make sure that you return
them the right way up.

SAFETY FIRST

Check the tides on the
Internet or at your local
tourist office before you go.
The best time to go is during
the very low tides. Head out
an hour or two before low
tide to give yourself plenty
of time to get back safely. Be
careful of the slippery rocks
near the shore.

DONE!

DATE
COMPLETED

88 MAKE AND PLAY LADYBIRD TIC-TAC-TOE

You might know this game as naughts and crosses. The ancient Romans called it Terni Lapilli. Whatever you call it, it's super cool when you have pet ladybird rocks to play with!

YOU WILL NEED:

- 10 smooth flat stones
- Acrylic paints in red, black, white, blue, and yellow
- Chalk
- Paintbrushes
- Sticks and twigs
- Garden string

1 Find 10 ladybird-shaped stones in your garden or park. Paint 5 of them red and the other 5 yellow. Give them a couple of coats of paint to make sure they're well covered. Let them dry thoroughly between coats.

2 Use chalk to mark the head and wing line on each. Use a thinner brush to paint over the wing line with black paint, then paint in the head. You can rub off the chalk when it's dry.

3 Now add the dots. You can either paint on the dots with a brush or dip a finger into the paint and finger paint them on.

4 When the black paint is dry, add other details – eyes, mouth, nose, and antenna. The end of the paintbrush is great for making dots for the antenna.

5 When you've painted all 10 stones, you have all the pieces for the game. Make the grid by crisscrossing sticks and branches on the ground. You can make them sturdy by tying them with string.

6 Play tic-tac-toe! One player uses the red ladybirds, the other uses the yellow ladybirds. Take it in turns to place a ladybird in a square. The first to get 3 in a row wins!

DONE!   DATE COMPLETED

89 GROW MINT TEA

Mint tea is refreshing, delicious, and good for you!
A pot of freshly grown mint makes your house or
garden smell wonderful too.

YOU WILL NEED:

To grow your mint:

- Small pot (30 cm is ideal)
- Compost
- Small mint plant (you can buy many different varieties)
- Small stones or gravel
- Sunny window ledge, patio, or doorstep

To make your tea:

- A bunch of mint leaves
- Sugar or honey to taste
- Boiling water (ask an adult to do this for you)
- Mug or a heatproof glass

1 If you can, plant your mint in spring, or in the fall if you're in a climate that is free of frost. Plant your mint 5 cm deep in a 30-cm pot.

2 Put your pot in a sunny position. Ideally, it will receive morning sunlight and have some shade in the afternoon. Keep it well watered so that the soil is always damp.

3 Keep the top of your plant well trimmed to stop it from growing too tall. This will encourage growth at the sides.

4 For your mint tea, pinch a stem or two of mint from your plant, and rinse under cold water. Crush the leaves a bit as you put them into the bottom of your mug to help bring out the minty taste and smell.

5 Ask an adult to boil a kettle and pour the boiling water over your leaves. Leave it to cool down a little before you try it!

6 Add sugar or honey to taste. You can even add a squeeze of citrus (lemon or lime) if you want to add a tasty zing!

WHY NOT?
Add to new potatoes or carrots? Mint can be used for all sorts of cooking. You can add it to cold drinks such as lemonade too.

DONE! DATE COMPLETED

90 GET WET IN THE WATER RELAY!

This is a fun game to play with a couple of friends on a hot day. You'll need a plastic drinking cup and a bucket each as well as a giant bucket of water. And yes – the water is supposed to drip down your nose!

1 Ask an adult to poke 6 holes into the sides of each cup using a thick sewing needle. Make sure there are the same number of holes in each player's cup!

2 Choose a grassy area with a lot of space. Put the empty buckets in a line on the ground a little apart from one another. Put the giant bucket full of water at the other end of that area.

3 Players start at the big bucket of water. When someone shouts GO, they fill their cups with water at the same time. The players hold their cups above their heads and run to their empty buckets.

4 As the players reach their buckets, they should tip any water left in their cup into it and race back to the other end. The first to fill his or her bucket right up to the top wins! On your marks, get set . . . GO!

DONE! DATE COMPLETED

WORK OUT THE AGE OF A TREE

If a tree has been cut down, you can work out how old it was when it died by counting its rings. But if the tree is alive, there's another way to calculate its age.

40IN
―――
1
= 40 YEARS OLD

1 Decide on the tree that you want to find the age of. Wrap your tape measure around the trunk, and measure its circumference, or girth.

2 If you've measured in centimetres, divide by 2.5. If you have measured in inches, divide this figure by 1. The growth of an average tree girth per year is 2.5 centimetres, or 1 inch. So a tree with a 40-cm (16-in) girth will be approximately 16 years old.

3 If you know the species of your tree, you can age it more accurately. For example, oaks and beeches grow approximately 1.75 cm per year. Pine trees grow about 3 cm per year, and sycamores grow around 2.75 cm per year. Divide by these figures instead of 2.5.

BEECH

SYCAMORE

OAK

PINE

DONE!

DATE COMPLETED

92 HANG A WREATH

Welcome visitors to your door by hanging a wreath! Use leaves and stems collected from your garden or local area at any time of the year. Berries and flowers add a great splash of colour.

YOU WILL NEED:

- Florist foam ring with a plastic bottom
- Ribbon
- Scissors
- Foliage, for example, sprigs of fir, holly, ivy, mistletoe, rosemary, lavender, flowers, berries – anything that you can find with a stem!

1 Collect foliage. Sprigs of fir, holly, and berried ivy all work well. But anything with a stem will work! Use scissors to cut stems about 10 cm long. Ask permission before you pick anything!

2 Remove 3 cm of leaves or needles from each sprig so that you have stems to press into the foam. Either trim with scissors or remove them with your fingers. Watch out! They can be prickly!

3 Float the foam ring face down into a bowl or sink of water and allow it to sink naturally. Do not force it under. After about a minute it will turn dark green. Take it out.

4 Insert sprigs of one plant into your foam at regular intervals. Angle the sprigs to follow the shape of the wreath.

5 Insert leaves or sprigs of different plants at different angles, still following the wreath's outline. Make sure you cover all parts of the foam equally. Keep going until you have filled all the gaps in the wreath.

6 Thread the ribbon through the centre of the wreath. Tie a knot at the top so that you can hang it. If you want to, tie a bow instead of a knot. Hang on your door to welcome all your visitors!

DONE!   DATE COMPLETED

93 PING A MASTERPIECE

This is fun, messy art, perfect for doing outdoors.
You'll ping a masterpiece together in no time!

YOU WILL NEED:

- Rubber bands (different thicknesses if possible)
- Sponge
- Different coloured paints
- Paintbrush
- Cardboard (for example, the side of a cereal box)
- White paper that is twice as wide as the cardboard
- Containers for paint mixing

1 Fold the white paper around the cardboard to cover both sides. Stretch and wrap the rubber bands over it to make a pattern of lines.

2 Squeeze coloured paints into different containers. Dip sponges into the paints and dab them onto the paper with the rubber bands. For clean colours, use a different sponge for each paint.

3 Use the paintbrush to drip some paint onto a couple of the bands and ping them. The colours will splash over the paper randomly.

4 Let your art dry on one side, and then paint the other. When the second side is dry, remove the rubber bands and unfold the paper to see the patterns you've created.

WHY NOT?
Use your rubber band art as wrapping paper or stationery?

DONE! DATE COMPLETED

GO POND DIPPING

94

Discover a hidden world in a pond. You'll need a net, a shallow tray, a magnifying glass, wellie boots, and a pond field guide.

1 First, fill your tray with pond water. Then gently sweep your net around the pond through the vegetation. Creatures live on the top, the middle, and the bottom of the pond, so make sure you sweep in all areas. You want to disturb some of the sediment at the bottom.

2 Turn your net inside out over your tray so that any creatures and plants fall out. What can you see? Don't forget to look under and on the vegetation. Creatures will hide in your tray just as they do in the pond. Can you identify any of them in your field guide?

SAFETY FIRST!
Always go pond dipping with an adult. Stand at the edge of the pond rather than wading in, and don't lean over too far. Always put the creatures back where you found them when you're done.

3 For a closer look, scoop up a creature and some water into a smaller pot with a lid. Use your magnifying glass and check your field guide to see what you've found!

DONE! | DATE COMPLETED

95 LAUNCH A VINEGAR ROCKET

Bicarbonate of soda and vinegar make brilliant rocket fuel! Try mixing them together in an empty drink bottle to launch your very own rocket.

YOU WILL NEED:

- 1 empty plastic bottle
- 1 piece of white tissue
- 1 cork
- 3 pencils
- Adhesive tape
- Bicarbonate of soda
- Vinegar
- Safety goggles

1 Tape the pencils to the side of the bottle in a triangle to make fins. The bottom ends of the pencils should be facing upwards. The ends should line up at the bottle top.

2 Make the bicarbonate of soda parcel. Put two large spoonfuls of bicarbonate of soda into the middle of the tissue. Fold the corners up and twist the wrap to hold the powder inside.

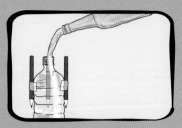

3 Fill the bottle about a third of the way up with vinegar. Any vinegar works, but white vinegar is less messy.

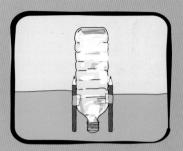

4 Make sure you are outside before you do this step. Carefully push the bicarbonate of soda parcel into the top of the bottle. Ask an adult to help you to push the cork firmly into the bottle top.

5 Gently shake the bottle, making sure you keep it away from your face. Quickly stand the rocket up on its fins and move away.

6 Stand well back and wait for LIFT-OFF!

HOW DOES IT WORK?

When the bicarbonate of soda and vinegar react, carbon dioxide is released, creating pressure in the bottle. When the pressure gets high enough, it will push the cork out and the pressure will force all of the liquid and gas out of the bottle very fast, making it shoot upwards.

SAFETY FIRST!

Always do this with an adult. Stay well away from the bottle. You MUST be outdoors in a large space.

DONE! DATE COMPLETED

96 MAKE A BIRD BATH

Birds might fly several miles to find clean drinking water. Why not tempt them into your garden or onto your balcony with a bird bath?

YOU WILL NEED:

- Plant pot or bucket
- Saucer (ideally with a rough surface)
- Garden paint
- Waterproof glue or tile adhesive
- Pebbles
- Water

1 Find an old plant pot or bucket. Turn it upside down and paint it. Be imaginative with colours, patterns, and pictures.

2 Now paint the saucer. Ideally use one with a rough surface for the birds' feet to grip without slipping. Terracotta plant saucers are perfect. Leave the pot and saucer to dry overnight.

3 Glue around the top of the upturned pot. Place the saucer on top, making sure that it is positioned in the middle. Press firmly, and allow the glue to set.

4 Find a safe place to put your birdbath. Nearby branches are useful for birds to hop to safety from a swooping bird of prey or a hungry cat!

5 Pile up some pebbles on one side of the saucer. The birds can perch on these. They will also provide a spot for insects to lie in the sun.

6 Fill the saucer with water, making sure that the pebbles are slightly above the waterline to make a perch. Perfect! The birds now have a spot to drink.

WHY NOT?
Set up a wildlife camera to record your visitors? You can note which birds come to visit during different times of the year!

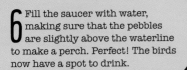

DONE!   DATE COMPLETED

97 CREATE A BOOT GARDEN

Don't get rid of your old wellie boots – use them to create an awesome garden! If you want to get really carried away, find more boots and shoes in your local charity shop.

1 Find some old wellie boots. If there aren't holes in them already, ask an adult to make some holes in the bottom to allow for drainage (using a hand drill and large drill bit).

2 Pour sand or grit into the bottom of each foot to add weight and stop them from falling over. It will also help with drainage. Fill them to the top with potting soil or compost.

3 Plant them with seeds, bulbs, or potting plants, and arrange them artistically in your garden. Don't forget to water them if it doesn't rain!

WHY NOT?
Fancy some mystery flora? When you next get home from a muddy walk, scrape the mud off the bottom of your boots and plant that. You'll be amazed at what might pop up!

☐ DONE!   DATE COMPLETED

PLAY SAND DARTS

Are you a devil on the dartboard? Or maybe you've never played? Try this version the next time you're on the beach. Try to beat your best score!

1 Collect a pile of small pebbles and shells. These will be your "darts". (Avoid large and heavy pebbles or rocks that could hurt someone by mistake.)

2 Use your finger or one of the pebbles to draw a circle in the sand, about the width of your foot. Draw 4 bigger circles around that circle.

3 Mark the circles with the points you can earn for each ring: 10, 20, 30, 40, and 50 (for the "bull's-eye" in the centre). Draw a line in the sand to stand behind for each throw.

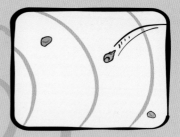

4 Take turns throwing your sand darts into the ring. Always throw underarm. Keep scores in the sand, and play to win!

DONE!

DATE COMPLETED

99 PLAY DROP CATCH

How good are you with a ball? Can you catch one on two knees, with one hand on the floor and both eyes closed?

1 Stand in a circle with some friends and space yourselves out equally. The further apart you are, the more challenging the game will be. Decide who is going to start, and give that person the ball.

2 The first person should throw the ball to another player in the circle. If that player catches it, he or she then throws it to another player, and so on.

3 The ball is thrown back and forth in the circle until someone drops it. The "dropper" has to pay a penalty and continue to play on one knee. Any other "droppers" pay the same penalty.

4 If players on one knee catch their next ball, they can stand back up again. But if they drop that one too, they pay another penalty and go down on two knees. On a third drop, the player on two knees should also put one hand to the ground; on a fourth drop, close one eye; and on a fifth drop, close both eyes! If players with penalties catch the ball again, they can remove one penalty – for example, if they're on two knees, one knee can come up again. The last player still in the game wins!

DONE!   DATE COMPLETED

PLAY HORSE

You just need a basketball, a basketball hoop, and a group of friends to play this game. Who will spell HORSE first?

1 Stand in a line – this will be the order for you to take your turn. The first player takes a shot at the basketball hoop. If he or she makes the shot, then the second player has to make the same type of shot, from the same place as the first player.

2 If player 2 makes the shot, then the third player has to make the same shot, and so on. If player 2 misses, then he or she gets a letter – first H, then an O, and so on, until it spells HORSE. If players spell out the whole word, then they are out of the game.

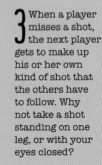

3 When a player misses a shot, the next player gets to make up his or her own kind of shot that the others have to follow. Why not take a shot standing on one leg, or with your eyes closed?

4 Keep playing until there is only one player left – this person is the winner!

DONE!

DATE COMPLETED

101 MAKE AN OUTDOOR SILHOUETTE THEATRE

Dusk and dark can be magical times outdoors. What better time to put on a shadow show for your family and friends? It can be quite simple . . . or simply epic!

YOU WILL NEED:

- An old sheet
- A big torch or outdoor lamp
- Sketch book and pencil
- Black card
- Scissors
- Bass fasterners (split pins)
- Wooden skewers or a thin garden cane
- Masking tape
- Light-coloured pencil or crayon
- Your imagination!

1 First, decide on the story that you are going to perform. Is it a well-known story, like a fairy tale? Or is it something you've made up yourself? Sketch the characters and props that you need.

2 Make your shadow puppets. For each character, draw a head and body onto the black card with the pencil or crayon. Include details, such as eyes, hair, and mouth.

3 Add limbs. Cut out arms and legs, and join them to your character's body with brass fasteners (split pins). This will mean that you can move them in the show.

DONE!   DATE COMPLETED

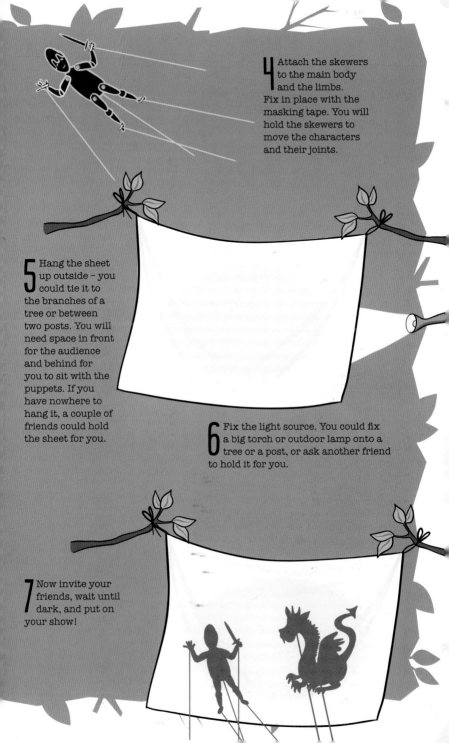

4 Attach the skewers to the main body and the limbs. Fix in place with the masking tape. You will hold the skewers to move the characters and their joints.

5 Hang the sheet up outside – you could tie it to the branches of a tree or between two posts. You will need space in front for the audience and behind for you to sit with the puppets. If you have nowhere to hang it, a couple of friends could hold the sheet for you.

6 Fix the light source. You could fix a big torch or outdoor lamp onto a tree or a post, or ask another friend to hold it for you.

7 Now invite your friends, wait until dark, and put on your show!

STAYING SAFE:
DOS AND DON'TS

 DO: Take care while using scissors and other sharp objects.

DO: Wear a helmet while riding a sled, bike, skateboard, etc.

DO: Always wear old clothes or an apron when doing art projects.

DO: Carefully follow the instructions and pay attention to any safety warnings.

 DON'T: Start a messy project without asking an adult.

DON'T: Go anywhere without telling an adult first!

ACKNOWLEDGEMENTS

Written by Susan Hayes
Design and illustration: Shahid Mahmood
Senior Designer: Katie Knutton
Senior Editor: Lydia Halliday
Editor: Fay Evans
Publisher: Donna Gregory